MW00779822

Why Don't We Ask Why?

ALSO BY VICTORY GURLEY JR.

Artificial Intelligence. REAL Results.

Buying When They Say "Don't Buy"

Why Don't We Ask Why?

Discovering Purpose Through
the Power of Curiosity

Victory J. Gurley Jr.

ISBN 979-8-218-42003-1
Paperback ISBN 979-8-326-18231-9
eBook ISBN 979-8-8693-2748-2

Printed in the United States of America

Book design by Victory Gurley Jr.

First Edition

DEDICATION

I want to dedicate this book to my mother, Yolanda, who I've witnessed battle and continually evolve, while simultaneously being the light for others stuck in dark places. We have both seen some dark moments, but you always shine your light when I need it most. I love you! #StayREAL

Character developed in the shadows of adversity illuminates the strongest 'why,' enabling one to endure any 'how' with unwavering resolve.

— Victory J. Gurley Jr.

TABLE OF CONTENTS

INTRODUCTION

Why? Take a moment to truly ponder this very simple yet profound question that binds us all within the vast wardrobe of existence where every thread is a life, and every color is a story. It's a question that echoes in the silent spaces between our thoughts, in the moments of solitude under the night sky, in the bustling streets of our cities, and in the quiet embrace of nature. "Why?" is not just a question; it is a journey. It's a quest that dares us to seek beyond the visible, to question the status quo, and to discover the truths that lie hidden beneath the surface of our daily lives.

As you stand at the threshold of this journey, imagine yourself at the edge of a vast forest. The path before you twists and turns into the unknown, blanketed in mist and mystery. This book is your invitation to embark on a voyage of discovery, not just through the pages of a story but through the layers of your own existence. As sentient beings, we are innately driven to seek purpose and to unravel the intricate threads that weave together our existence. How do we discern our true path amid the clamor of external influences? How do we reconcile the teachings bestowed upon us with the authentic lessons we learn along our individual journeys? And perhaps most importantly, why do we seldom pause to question the foundations upon which our beliefs are built?

This narrative will not promise you answers to your life's uncertainties, but it will provide a roadmap and compass. Through the intertwined lives of Ajani, serving as the embodiment of our collective humanity; Zuri, as the mirror of divine leadership; and Ola, gracefully epitomizing the essence of spirituality and purpose within our earthly realm, you are invited to explore the depths of your own 'whys.' Through the divergent interactions of these three distinct entities, the goal is for you, the reader, to extract the wisdom that resides within you and find your place in the grand scheme of existence.

Your first introduction will be to Ajani, a curious 33-year-old entrepreneur on a quest to unravel the perplexing threads of his existence. Ajani has carried the weight of childhood traumas and burdens that have shaped the lens through which he perceives the world. Living in a society plagued by delusional disorders, he is confronted with the pressures of conformity, the relentless pursuit of success, and crippling deceit. Yet, beneath the surface of his struggles, a flicker of curiosity persists as a yearning to discover his true purpose and to transcend the limitations imposed upon him by the society he was born into. For Ajani, the journey towards self-discovery is a battleground between the teachings of society and the whisperings of his soul. Born with a blank moral slate, he finds himself navigating the maze of conflicting ideologies and societal expectations. But as he delves deeper into his quest, eventually crossing paths with Zuri and others, he begins to question the nature of his existence and the lessons he has been taught.

Zuri, a majestic creature, whose presence graces the vast wilderness, embodies the gentle strength and unwavering resilience that exists within the animal kingdom. Born innocent, she possesses an innate knowledge, an instinct that guides her from the moment she takes her first steps. In the embrace of her herd, Zuri learns the essential survival skills and the intricate dynamics of her social community. She discovers the interconnectedness that binds every member of her kind, forging deep bonds of trust and understanding.

In the wake of loss, Zuri is forced to undergo a profound transformation, as she embarks on a quest of survival, battling with the thirst for vengeance and the discovery of her purpose. In her pursuit, she encounters the complexities of survival and the delicacy of existence, all while trying to learn the importance of codependency among other beings sharing the land in which she roams. Her paths cross with those of Ajani and Ola, entities vastly different in form but connected by the threads of existence they share. Through these connections, Zuri's story becomes a mirror reflecting the shared trials and triumphs that life presents, regardless of form. It is in the intertwining of their destinies that the universal themes of loss, growth, and the discovery of purpose emerge, revealing the unity that underlies the diversity of their experiences.

Ola stands as a symbol of tranquility and unwavering purpose within the natural world. Anchored firmly in the soil, she observes the endless cycles of existence that unfold around her. From the modest beginnings of a small seed, Ola's life is shaped by the elemental dance of sunlight and rain, each season intricately weaving the fabric of her being. Her growth is a silent spectacle of nature's marvel and is both a solitary and a collective endeavor. Through the essential acts of cross-pollination and the nurturing forces of the environment, Ola matures to offer her gifts to the world, which are symbolic of the nourishment and renewal she provides. Her presence in the landscape is a gentle reminder of the beauty and balance achieved when one embraces their intrinsic role in the tapestry of life.

Together, their stories intertwine, painting a rich narrative of life's complexities and the universal quest for meaning. As Ajani ventures beyond the confines of societal expectations, you, too, may find the courage to question the boundaries of your present reality. In Zuri's resilience and wisdom, you may discover the strength to face your challenges with grace and to lead with compassion. And in Ola's silent, steadfast presence, you may learn the value of deep connections, of enduring growth, and of living in your divine purpose in the profound alignment with the cycles and whispers of the natural world.

Through the interplay of these captivating narratives and introspective reveries, this book compels you to reflect upon the influences that shape your own path. It inspires you to transcend the limitations of societal teachings and embrace the pursuit of knowledge that lies beyond established norms. In a world where the clamor of external influences often overshadows genuine learning, let us embark on this odyssey together. Let us rediscover the interconnectedness of all life forms, transcending boundaries and rediscovering the profound beauty that resides in every corner of existence.

Let the pages that follow be the steppingstones on your path and each chapter, a milepost on your journey. May you find, within the fabric of this narrative, the threads that resonate with your soul, inspire you to transcend the limitations of societal teachings, and embrace the pursuit of knowledge that lies beyond established norms. Remember, the quest for "Why" is not about reaching a destination; it's about embracing the journey, with all its twists and turns, its revelations, and mysteries. It's about the moments of clarity, the connections forged along the way, and the understanding that, in the end, the journey itself is the answer.

Now, as you prepare to enter the lives of these three sentient beings, imagine the dawn breaking over the horizon, casting the first light on your path. Remember to keep your mind open, your heart pure, and your spirit willing to explore the infinite possibilities that lie ahead. Challenge yourself to recognize the deep symbolism throughout these narratives to fully embrace the similarities within your own life. The journey ahead is yours to take, the questions yours to ask, and the discoveries yours to make. The time has come to ask why, to illuminate the path to our divine purpose, and to embark on a journey that will transform our lives forever.

A few whys to consider as you journey through the pages:

1. Why do we often fear the unknown more than the discomfort of remaining in familiar but unfulfilling situations?

2. Why do we allow societal expectations to dictate our choices and dreams, even when they clash with our true desires?

3. Why is it that in our quest for happiness, we frequently overlook the simple joys that surround us daily?

4. Why do we struggle with letting go of past hurts, allowing them to shape our present and future?

5. Why do we measure our worth by our productivity or financial success, rather than our personal fulfilment and impact on others?

6. Why is it easier to offer understanding and forgiveness to others, yet so hard to extend the same grace to ourselves?

7. Why do we fear vulnerability, seeing it as a weakness, when it's the birthplace of connection and creativity?

8. Why do we keep waiting for the "right moment" to pursue our passions, not realizing that time is the one thing we can never get back?

9. Why do we often feel alone in our struggles, forgetting that shared experiences connect us deeply with others?

10. Why do we resist change, knowing that growth and new beginnings are often on the other side of our comfort zone?

PART I: AJANI

Ajani
Origin: Nigerian, Yoruba
Meaning: The victor; He who wins the struggle

1 WHO IS AJANI?

In the urban heartlands where Ajani's story began, he learned life's earliest lessons. His parents, two souls bound by a sense of duty rather than love, instilled in him a dualistic worldview. His mother, a gentle soul, sang him songs of the spirits that moved the seas and stars, instilling in him a reverence for the unseen. Her unwavering faith endowed him with a spiritual lens through which to view the world.

Meanwhile, his father, a stern yet scorned soul, remained mentally absent from Ajani's life. His persona and approach to fatherhood provided Ajani with the traumas he carried into adulthood, as well as the insight and motivation he carried into his own transition into fatherhood. His parents' tempestuous relationship and inherent dichotomy laid the groundwork for Ajani's understanding of life and engraved the first questions on his blank moral slate.

In the microcosm of Ajani's youth, two powerful forces battled within the walls of a home that creaked with the weight of unspoken dreams and open-ended sighs. Ajani learned to navigate life's ebbs and flows, his existence swinging between the fervent encouragement of his mother and the oppressive doubt cast by his father.

His early years were marked by the struggle to find a semblance of peace in a home where harmony was a fleeting guest. The athletic arenas and sketch pads became his sanctuaries, places where he could sculpt an identity untainted by the dissonance of his home life. It was within these mediums that he first tasted small successes, basking in the glow of athletic achievement and the promise of a future brighter than the shadowed corners of his youth.

On the football field and basketball court, Ajani discovered the sweet rush of victory—the way his body could sprint past limitations and how each touchdown and jump shot whispered promises of a future unfettered by the doubts that clouded his home. Yet each triumph was shadowed by a specter of uncertainty.

His father, a man who viewed the world through lenses tinted with pragmatism, saw little value in the dreams of his son. Each accolade Ajani brought home was met not with cheers, but with the cold questioning gaze of a man who believed the true arenas of life were far removed from the frivolous pursuits of sports and arts.

This dichotomy of parental influence left Ajani caught in an emotional tug-of-war. His mother's words were soft and uplifting, pushing him towards the light of his potential. Yet, they were like candles in the storm of his father's relentless doubt—a storm that extinguished flickers of hope with gusts of harsh reality checks. Ajani's confidence thus became a castle built on sand, vulnerable to the tides of his father's skepticism.

As a defense, Ajani learned to fold inward, to shield his aspirations within the fortress of his mind. His extroverted spirit, once as free as the strokes of paint on his canvas, began to recoil. The boy who once shared his sketches and trophies began to bury them in the depths of his drawers, away from the scrutiny that turned pride into uncertainty.

Ajani's introversion became his armor; silence, his response to the fear of being belittled. He nurtured his dreams in private, letting them bloom in the safety of his mind where they could not be trampled by his father's heavy-footed doubts. It was a solitary existence, one where the cheering crowds of his victories echoed only within him.

Yet, in the quiet of his own company, Ajani found a friend in solitude. His inner world flourished with the vibrancy of his hidden talents. He ran faster in his mind than he ever could on the football field; his painted worlds were more vivid than those limited by the edges of his canvas. But within this hidden refuge, Ajani also faced a looming question—a question that would follow him into adulthood: Could he ever bridge the gap between the life he was living and the life he dreamed of?

Ajani continued to grow amidst the cacophony of city life, where dreams were as present as the graffiti on the walls, both vivid and expressive, yet often overlooked. Another one of his childhood struggles was against the societal currents that threatened to sweep away the identity he was trying to forge.

Success in his early years was defined narrowly by societal metrics, such as a college education, a high-paying job, and the mirage of financial freedom. Ajani pursued these with a relentless zeal, and by the time he donned his cap and gown as an exceptional high school graduate on his way to a prestigious university, he felt the sweet taste of success. But this success was transient, a mere prelude to the complexities of life awaiting him.

The struggle of his youth laid a complex foundation for the man Ajani would become. It was a foundation marked by the resilience of a spirit that refused to be extinguished, a testament to the power of belief in oneself amidst the chaos of doubting voices. As the chapters of his life unfolded, the memories of those early successes, shadowed by paternal doubt, would serve as silent guardians of his journey towards self-discovery—a journey to reclaim his voice and the power to define his worth.

Ajani's first fall as an adult was as silent as it was devastating. The expectation had been set high; as the first in his lineage poised to conquer the academic world, his every step was watched, weighed, and measured. Within the newfound freedoms of campus life, the rigid discipline that had brought him to this threshold began to waver. The structures of his previous life seemed distant, and the allure of independence, with its manifold distractions, beckoned him away from his studies.

His descent was not a plummet but a gentle drift away from the path he and those before him had envisioned. The libraries and lecture halls, once the arenas of his dreams, became reminders of a battle he felt he was losing. Ajani's focus dimmed, smudged by the haze of late-night escapades, the camaraderie of newfound friendships, and the exploration of his boundaries. Schoolwork, once the cornerstone of his daily life, now sat on the back burner, simmering on low, often forgotten.

As the semesters rolled by, the reality of his choices began to crystallize. Grades, those numerical gatekeepers of academic validation, reflected a story Ajani could hardly recognize, in the presence of missed opportunities and misplaced priorities. The moment of reckoning came like a cold dawn; Ajani knew he could no longer carry on this way. In a decision that echoed with a mix of defeat and defiance, he withdrew from college, stepping away from the expectations and entering a limbo of self-doubt and perceived failure.

The aftermath was a quiet, personal turbulence. Ajani grappled with the duality of his actions. How could the search for freedom lead to such a profound sense of entrapment? The freedom he had embraced now mocked him, a cruel joke at the expense of his future. He felt the sting of disappointment, not just his own but that which he read in the eyes of those depending on him to change the family trajectory. Ajani's self-concept, once rooted in the prospect of academic and subsequent professional success, now bore the heavy watermark of his departure from college.

Yet, it was within this space of failure that Ajani's resilience began to kindle a spark. It was faint at first, the kind of light one struggles to see unless enveloped in darkness. He began to understand that this detour could be a route to a different kind of enlightenment, one not measured by degrees and diplomas, but by self-education and the courage to forge a new path.

Ajani's journey through adversity was a slow and deliberate ascent, marked by a period of deep reflection that transformed days into months and months into years. This time of self-reflection and personal development was not merely a pause in his life, but a necessary unraveling of the preconceived notions of success that had been imposed upon him.

Who said that institutional education resulted in financial success? Is that really a requirement? To retrieve his answer, Ajani began a deep dive into the rise of some modern-day businessmen to include Bill Gates, Steve Jobs, and Mark Zuckerberg, none of whom completed their college education in the traditional sense. These discoveries served as beacons of inspiration for Ajani. Those who had achieved the type of financial success that he envisioned for himself did so without being traditional scholars, but instead, rebels who were never afraid to bet on themselves.

Bill Gates, who left Harvard University to co-found Microsoft, taught Ajani the value of vision and the importance of seizing opportunities with both hands. Gates's ability to look beyond the present and envision a world where personal computing would be accessible to the masses was a lesson in forward-thinking and innovation. Ajani absorbed the lesson that groundbreaking success often requires stepping off the beaten path and pursuing one's vision with unwavering dedication.

From Steve Jobs, who departed from Reed College only to become a co-founder of Apple, Ajani learned the significance of passion and design in crafting products that resonate with users on a deep emotional level. Jobs's journey underscored the importance of marrying technology with art to create products that are not just functional but aspirational. Ajani saw in Jobs's career a blueprint for building brands that stand at the intersection of innovation and creativity, where the value offered transcends the product itself.

Mark Zuckerberg's decision to drop out of Harvard University to focus fully on Facebook revealed to Ajani the power of connectivity and the potential of the digital age to bring the world closer. Zuckerberg's journey illustrated the importance of adaptability and the need to continually evolve in response to the changing digital landscape. From him, Ajani gleaned insights into the dynamics of social platforms and the vast potential of the internet as a tool for creating communities and fostering communication.

In studying these titans of the tech industry, Ajani didn't just learn about the paths they took, but about the mindset that propelled them forward. He realized that financial success in the modern world isn't tethered to the traditional pillars of academic credentials but to the courage to innovate, the passion to pursue one's dreams, and the resilience to overcome setbacks. Their success stories also highlight the complex balance between ambition and its impact on ethics, competition, and personal relationships.

Equipped with these lessons, Ajani set out to forge his path, drawing from Gates's visionary outlook, Jobs's creative genius, and Zuckerberg's mastery of connectivity. He built his arsenal of business acumen and mental fortitude, ready to navigate the perilous seas of entrepreneurship with a blend of inspiration from some of the poster boys for modern-day wealth and from the unique insights gained from his own journey. Ajani's story is a vibrant mosaic of learning, reflecting the multitude of ways success can be achieved when one is bold enough to define it on their own terms.

As he delved into the essence of his aspirations, Ajani simultaneously carved a path within the corporate world, a realm where he meticulously gathered more secrets of success that lay hidden beneath the surface. His tenure in the corporate sphere was a masterclass in capitalism, relationship building, and politics, where each day presented opportunities to absorb the strategies and insights of industry veterans.

These experiences were not just lessons in business but in life, teaching him the value of informal learning, the power of networking, and the importance of strategic thinking. As Ajani climbed the corporate ladder, he not only secured his footing but also forged invaluable relationships that would later serve as the foundation for his entrepreneurial endeavors.

It was against this backdrop of growth and learning that Ajani ventured into entrepreneurship. Straddling the demands of his corporate role and the challenges of nurturing a fresh, unseasoned business, he embarked on a dual quest for personal and professional fulfillment. His business, a reflection of his yearning for financial autonomy, became the vessel through which he could channel the wealth of knowledge he had amassed.

This new venture was more than just a pursuit of success; it was an ode to the dreams of his younger self, a bridge to his origins, and a testament to the transformative power of adversity. This served as a vivid illustration of how confronting challenges head-on can lead to a redefinition of success, one that resonates with the present version of ourselves.

Amidst the whirlwind of balancing his burgeoning entrepreneurial venture with the demands of his corporate job, Ajani encountered a pivotal moment of clarity. The stories of Gates, Jobs, and Zuckerberg whispered to him not just in moments of aspiration but in times of deep reflection. They all shared a common thread—a decisive leap into the unknown fueled by an unwavering belief in their vision.

Ajani realized that to scale his business, to truly walk in the footsteps of the titans he admired, he needed to embrace the same level of commitment. It meant leaving the safety net of corporate America behind, a daunting prospect that promised the freedom to fully invest in his own dream.

The decision wasn't easy. The corporate world had provided not just a steady income but a sense of identity. Yet, the more Ajani pondered, the clearer it became that his future lay not in climbing someone else's ladder but in building his own. It was a leap of faith, inspired by the legends who had once stood at similar crossroads, choosing potential over security.

Over the course of four more transformative years, Ajani's entrepreneurial venture unfolded like a well-scripted narrative from the pages of an inspiring biography. With the corporate shackles cast aside, he immersed himself in his business, channeling every ounce of his being into its growth. It was a period marked by relentless dedication, strategic ingenuity, and a series of calculated risks that would eventually catapult his company into the seven-figure echelon.

Ajani's journey to financial success was not merely about profit margins and revenue streams; it was a quest to materialize the dreams of his younger self. The sketches of opulence he had once drawn with the naive strokes of a child began to take form in the tangible world. The acquisition of a sprawling house, with the childhood desire of an in-ground pool, marked the first of many "trophies" he had aspired to. It stood as a testament to his achievements, its waters reflecting not just the sky above but the depth of his journey.

His collection soon expanded to include dream cars that were once posters on his bedroom wall—each vehicle a milestone symbolizing the various phases of his business's evolution. Jewelry that glittered with the promise of success adorned his wrists, serving as a constant reminder of where he had been and what he had accomplished.

With success also came the companionship of beautiful women, each drawn to the aura of a man who had seemingly cracked the code of life. For Ajani, these achievements were the embodiment of the "American Dream," a dream that had been redefined on his own terms. He had not just attained financial freedom but had crafted a lifestyle that mirrored the aspirations of his youth. Every morning as he gazed out at the expanse of his estate, he felt a surge of satisfaction—a confirmation that he had indeed made it. The luxuries that surrounded him were more than just material possessions; they were symbols of his resilience, his hard work, and his unyielding belief in his vision.

This period of opulence, however, was more than a personal triumph; it was a living, breathing manifestation of what could be achieved when one dares to venture beyond the familiar confines of societal expectations. Ajani had not only scaled his business to remarkable heights but had also ascended to a version of success that was intricately aligned with the deepest desires of his heart. In his reflection, he saw not just the entrepreneur he had become but the child who dared to dream, proving that the essence of the "American Dream" lies in the courage to pursue one's own definition of success.

As Ajani reveled in the pinnacle of his achievements, basking in the glory of his hard-earned paradise, he unwittingly overlooked the shadows that danced at the border of his success. Unseen, dark spirits of greed and betrayal lurked, drawn to the brilliance of his ascent, waiting for a moment of vulnerability to strike. It was in this oversight, this naive belief in the purity of those closest to him, that Ajani's fortress of dreams would soon face its gravest threat.

The architect of this impending doom was none other than his long-time accountant, a woman he had once trusted with his life, seeing her as a partner in both business and the celebration of his success. Alongside her, one of his business partners, whom Ajani had regarded as a pillar of support in his entrepreneurial journey, wove a web of deceit that was as intricate as it was devastating. Together, they orchestrated an embezzlement scheme that was both bold and cunning. Under the facade of expanding the business and exploring new ventures, they siphoned funds into shadow accounts, meticulously covering their tracks with forged documents and falsified reports. The operation was carried out with surgical precision, exploiting Ajani's focus on growth and innovation, leveraging his trust to mask their actions.

The revelation came crashing down on Ajani like the waves of a tsunami, unraveling the tapestry of his success thread by thread. An anonymous tip, a paper trail followed in disbelief, led to the heart-wrenching discovery. The numbers didn't lie, nor did the evidence that painted a clear picture of betrayal. The scheme, if left unchecked, had the power to collapse everything Ajani had built, to reduce his dreams to ruins.

In this moment of betrayal, Ajani faced not just the potential loss of his company but the shattering of personal relationships he held dear. The realization that those he loved and relied on could orchestrate such deceit was a blow far more devastating than any financial loss. It was a test of his tenacity, a challenge to the very foundations upon which he had built his life and identity, one that he could never have learned in the corporate world or a classroom.

In the aftermath, Ajani found himself standing amidst the ruins of what he had built, faced with a choice—to let this setback define his journey or to rise from it more determined than ever. Now, standing at the threshold of what he once defined as success, Ajani felt the familiar tug of existential turmoil. The corporate accolades and the comforting weight of wealth could not fill the void that spread like a silent chasm within him.

He began to reflect on the time invested, energy exerted, and relationships sacrificed to attain that amount of wealth, and in the same thought, he reflected on how it was snatched away in the blink of an eye. Had he reached the summit of his life's aspirations, or was there a greater purpose awaiting his discovery?

Ajani's narrative is an intricate dance of shadows and light. His story serves as an allegory for the human experience, a reflection of our own struggles to find balance between achieving and being, owning and knowing, succeeding and fulfilling. Through Ajani's eyes, we are invited to examine the very fabric of our being, to unravel the threads of existence, and to weave a garment of life that is uniquely ours. As you, the reader, turn the next pages of Ajani's life, presented from his first-person perspective, you are asked to journey within, to discover your own set of 'whys' and to embrace the vast potential that life offers. Ajani's evolution is a mirror reflecting our collective quest for deeper meaning, challenging us to rise above the adversity and soar into the realms of purpose and possibility.

2 WHY AM I HERE?

Have you ever looked at your present life and asked yourself, "Why am I here?" Not necessarily here as in here on Earth, but here as in this present stage of life and here in this current situation. I began doing that amid some unexpected betrayal and chaos. At some point, I naively convinced myself that struggle and chaos were in my rearview mirror, never to be seen again. Boy, was I wrong.

In the eyes of society, I am living the "American Dream." I am a successful entrepreneur, world traveler, and arguably one of the most eligible bachelors walking God's green earth. Of course, I've had my fair share of skirmishes that served as preludes to my success.

My life, from the outside, was a meticulously curated exhibit, displaying each success as a shiny accolade hanging on the walls of my personal museum. People would often comment on how everything I touched turned to gold. But beneath the sheen, the golden touch had its price. Sacrifices were made, relationships were tested, and integrity was often questioned. It was a relentless pursuit, chasing horizons that seemed to stretch further away with every milestone reached.

The trouble with the pursuit of success is that it's insatiable.

It's like drinking saltwater when you're thirsty. It's like climbing to the top of a mountain just to look up and discover that there's always going to be a higher peak to conquer. With each peak scaled, I expected to find solace, a sense of fulfillment, but what awaited was more mountainous terrain. The hustle became a habit, a relentless forward motion that knew of no limits or expiration. But success breeds envy, sometimes even in those closest to you. It started with small discrepancies, numbers that didn't add up, invoices that seemed out of place. I overlooked these, trusting not only in the systems we had built but in the foundation of our friendships.

The day I found out about the embezzlement was the day my reality crumbled. It wasn't just about the money, even though it was a substantial blow. It was the realization that the trust, the years of camaraderie, and shared dreams could be traded so cheaply. I had been blindsided by my own faith in people, and it shook me to my core. The sense of betrayal lingered like a stain that no amount of success could cleanse.

That's when the questions started. Why did I chase what I chased? Was it for the thrill of success or the fear of insignificance? Why did I work the way I worked—relentlessly, obsessively, as if each deal was a verdict on my worth? I began to replay every decision, every sacrifice.

I had traded precious, irrecoverable time for wealth. I missed gatherings, birthdays, and holiday toasts over the hum of my laptop. The 'nos' I dished out to loved ones piled up like a ledger, a stark record of my skewed priorities. And what was it all for? The opulent house felt more like a mausoleum than a home, the fancy cars were just metal on wheels, and the designer clothes were mere fabric. They were possessions that I had ascribed meaning to, a meaning that now seemed hollow. The betrayal made me question not just my judgment of character but my entire value system.

It was this line of questioning that brought me to the

decision that would alter the trajectory of my life. I needed to get away for a while. Not to escape my problems but to face them head-on, in a space where the distractions of my life could not follow me. It was a pilgrimage for clarity, a journey not measured by the miles I would travel, but by the internal distances I would traverse within myself.

I needed to strip away the layers of noise, the unending buzz of the city, the relentless stream of emails, the incessant calls, and meetings that filled my days with urgency but left my nights echoing with emptiness. I craved the silence that would allow me to hear my own thoughts again, to listen to the voice inside that had been drowned out by the roar of success. So, I booked a flight; a flight to a place where the skyscrapers didn't block the sky and the air wasn't thick with entitlement and ambition. I sought sanctuary where the pace of life was dictated not by stock market fluctuations or closing deals but by the rising and setting of the sun.

As my departure date drew near, I felt an odd mixture of apprehension and relief. There was fear in the unknown and in stepping away from a life I had so meticulously built. Yet, there was also an intense sense of liberation in acknowledging that the life I built may not have been erected on the foundations I truly value. The night before I left, I stood in the expanse of my living room, the moonlight casting long shadows over the cold marble floors, and allowed myself a moment of vulnerability. I allowed myself to feel the hurt of the betrayal, the weight of the loneliness that had crept into my life, the quiet despair of a path that had led me away from who I once thought I would be.

I thought of my friend, my former business partner. In the stillness, I tried to understand what led him down that path. Greed? Desperation? I realized I would never fully know, and perhaps understanding him was not the key to my own peace. Forgiveness, however, was. It was not a forgiveness born of condonation; it was one of release, freeing myself from the chains of bitterness that had begun to encircle my heart.

In that moment, a quote from an old mentor came to me: "Success without fulfillment is the ultimate failure." I had chased and achieved every traditional and self-proclaimed metric of success, yet I felt a void where fulfillment should have resided. I needed to find out if I could fill that void not with more success but with more substance. I believed that substance to be present in a land far from where I resided.

3 THE JOURNEY

My eyes snapped open to the urgent chime of my phone's alarm, piercing the still darkness of my bedroom. From the moment I started packing my backpack with essentials, each item seemed to weigh more than usual, each one laden with my unresolved issues and silent anxieties.

As my driver pulled up, I hopped in and we were off. The drive to the airport was supposed to be straightforward. However, just as my mind began to wander through the fog of my thoughts, I realized the driver had missed the airport exit. My heart dropped with the car as we passed the sign.

"Come on, man! You missed the exit!" My voice came out harsher than I intended, echoing the bubbling frustration within me.

"I'm really sorry, sir," the driver replied, his eyes briefly meeting mine in the rearview mirror. "I'll get us back on track right away."

As he maneuvered through an alternative route, his repeated apologies became a soft background noise to the growing storm inside my head. Every minute we were delayed felt like an added weight, reflecting the pressures piling up in my life, which found an outlet in my sharp words to a respectable man who was just trying to help.

We made it to the airport with moments to spare. I leapt from the car, my backpack swinging as I sprinted through the terminal. I dashed through the security checkpoint, thanks to pre-check. I arrived at the gate just as the gate agent was about to close the door.

Breathless, I handed her my boarding pass as she cracked a knowing smile. "Just in the nick of time, huh?"

"Sometimes, I like to live life on the edge," I replied, grateful for the agent's lighthearted touch, easing some of my stress.

I made my way down the ramp, onto the plane, and into my window seat. I felt my body anchor down, but my mind was still airborne, caught between the clouds above and the chaotic streets below. The steady hum of the plane's engines as we took off did little to quiet the storm of doubts and what-ifs raging inside me, but it was too late to turn back now.

Mid-flight, the woman sitting next to me seemed to notice the tension radiating off me. Her voice was soft, yet clear, tinged with genuine concern, "Business or pleasure?"

I turned to her, managing a small smile. "I'm temporarily escaping from reality, so it's supposed to be pleasure, but we'll see how pleasurable it actually ends up being."

"That's quite common, you know," she responded, her tone warm and understanding. "But sometimes, our escape is just a detour back to ourselves. What's weighing on you, if you don't mind me asking?"

Her question made me hesitate, but something about the vast open sky made it feel safe to open up. "It's everything. Work, life... I feel like I'm at a crossroad and questioning which way to go."

She nodded thoughtfully and then offered, "We all face crossroads. The key isn't just choosing a path but understanding why it's our path. Have you ever really asked yourself why you're at this particular crossroad?"

Her simple question caught me off guard. It was the very question I had been avoiding. Our conversation deepened into discussions about choices, about disguising duties as desires, and about seeking genuine fulfillment beyond what society expects. As the flight carried on, my chat with the lovely woman peeled back layers of introspection I had long ignored, setting the groundwork for the journey of self-discovery that awaited me.

The flight was long, but my thoughts were an even longer journey. They spanned the expanse of my life, pausing at each significant milestone, each crossroad, and every high and low.

By the time the plane touched down on the runway, I was miles away from solving the puzzle of my discontent, but I felt that I was closer than I had ever been before. My destination was as far from my world as I could imagine. No tall buildings, no crime-filled streets, just endless horizons and skies that seemed to promise the possibility of answers. It was here that I hoped to find the space to rediscover the parts of myself that had been lost in the 'American Dream.'

As I disembarked from the plane, the cool breeze greeted me with a gentle caress, unlike the harsh winds of the city. I took a deep breath, allowing the fresh air to fill my lungs and slowly exhale the accumulated stress of urban life. This place was a stark contrast to the hustle and bustle I was accustomed to. Here, nature was in command, with sprawling fields, towering trees, and a vast sky that stretched endlessly.

Stepping into the small airport terminal, I was struck by the simplicity and quietude. The slow pace was not just in the movement of the people but in their demeanor—a sharp

24

departure from the urgency that characterized every interaction back home. Here, people had time. Time to smile, time to chat, and time to live.

I picked up my rental car, a modest SUV perfect for the rugged terrain, and drove towards the small cottage I had rented. The drive was therapeutic, with the landscape rolling by like a series of paintings, each more serene than the last. The road meandered through hills and alongside rivers, each turn revealing scenes that seemed painted for tranquility.

Upon arriving at the cottage, I was welcomed by Mrs. Martin, the owner, who lived nearby. Her warm smile and hearty handshake were infused with a kindness that was almost forgotten in city life. "Welcome to your haven," she said, handing me the keys. "I hope you find what you're looking for here."

The cottage itself was rustic and charming, with wood beams and a stone fireplace. It was cozy and unpretentious, a perfect space for reflection. After settling in, I stood at the edge of a nearby cliff, looking out over the valley below. The view was breathtaking, a vast expanse of nature untouched by the hand of man.

As the sun began to set, casting a golden glow over the landscape, I felt a peace I hadn't known in years. The quiet of the surroundings allowed me to hear the stirrings of my own heart, the voices of my deeper desires that had been drowned out by the noise of ambition and societal expectations.

That evening, as I sat by the fireplace, journal in hand, I began to write. Not about business strategies or meetings, but about my feelings, my fears, and my hopes. It was a raw outpouring of everything I had bottled up over the years. Each word that flowed onto the paper lightened my soul, as if I was shedding the weights that had anchored me to a life of superficial success.

Over the days that followed, I immersed myself in the natural beauty around me. I took long walks in the woods, sat by the riverbank watching the water flow, and spent nights looking at the stars. Each experience was a step towards healing, a step towards understanding the true essence of my being.

I met locals who lived not for wealth or recognition, but for the joy of living. Their lives were simple, yet rich in ways that money couldn't buy. Their stories and perspectives challenged my own, pushing me to reconsider what I valued most. Through these interactions, I realized how much of my life had been lived on autopilot, guided by a set of societal norms that no longer resonated with me.

I learned to appreciate the art of doing nothing, to see it not as idleness but as a vital act of self-recovery which would allow for self-discovery. In the quiet moments, I rediscovered a passion for painting, something I hadn't realized I'd lost in my ascent up the wealth ladder.

The brushstrokes felt like a language I had forgotten I could speak, each color a word, each canvas a sentence of the story I was beginning to write for myself. It was during these moments, with a paintbrush in hand and the vast sky above me, that the answer to "Why am I here?" began to take shape.

I was here to heal, to grow, to learn that life's truest success is not quantifiable. The definition of success is also one that alters with each phase we enter in life. It is the joy found in creation, the peace that comes with acceptance, and the love that builds when shared.

Yet, the journey inward was not without its battles. I grappled with the shadows of doubt that lurked in the corners of my mind, the whispers of fear that questioned whether I could ever return to my old life, whether I even wanted to. The nights were the hardest, when the quiet around me gave way to the clamor within.

I journaled eagerly and that discipline became my anchor in the rainstorm of self-reflection. Each entry was a step towards understanding, a mile walked on the path to a different kind of enlightenment. I wrote about the days and the nights, about the people and their stories, about the stillness of the land and the conversations that filled the air with a texture I had never felt back home. In my journal, I confessed to my fears and my dreams, to my disappointments and my hopes.

It became clear that the betrayal was not just a fracture in my past, but a fracture that ran deep, questioning the very ground I stood on. It wasn't just about the money or the breach of trust, but how closely I had tied my identity to my achievements and how fragile that made me.

Through the ink, I began to sketch out the man I wanted to become. He was less armored by achievements and more adorned by genuine human connections, less driven by the need to be seen as successful and more by the desire to be grounded in real joy and purpose. As I wrote, I realized that my journey to this far-off place was not an escape, but a pilgrimage towards something greater than external success. It was a journey towards inner peace, towards a life where 'why am I here?' became not a question of doubt but one of direction and intent.

It dawned on me that the quiet of this place was not emptiness, but the fullness of life in its simplest form. It was a life where success was measured not in ledger lines but in laughter lines, not in bank balances but in balanced hearts. I began to appreciate the interconnectedness of the world.

As I continued my journey of self-discovery, this new world beckoned with its rich recipe of cultures, histories, and landscapes waiting to be explored. Each destination held the promise of profound insights and transformative experiences, guiding me further along the path of understanding and enlightenment, but none more than the walking safari, I stumbled across on my morning jog. It was a no brainer. I'm in this land of breathtaking natural beauty and exotic wildlife, so I would be a fool to not experience it up close.

That morning, as the first light of dawn crept across the land, casting long shadows and painting the world in hues of gold and amber, I found myself at a crossroads of introspection and anticipation. The decision to join the walking safari was not merely a choice to witness the majesty of nature but a step deeper into the wilderness of my own being. As I laced up my shoes and set out on my jog, the crisp air of the early morning served as a reminder of the freshness of beginnings, of the endless possibilities that lay ahead.

My mind, usually a whirlwind of thoughts and reflections, found a rare moment of clarity in the rhythm of my stride. The journey of self-discovery I had embarked upon, armed with nothing but a journal and my paints, had led me to moments of profound self-awareness and a yearning to peel back the layers of my existence. Now, as the opportunity to venture into the heart of the savannah presented itself, it felt like a metaphorical journey mirroring my own – a venture into the unknown in search of something more, something deeper. The solitude of my recent days, filled with strokes of paint and words on a page, had set the stage for this moment, preparing me to face the wilderness not just outside, but within.

Arriving at the meet-up point, I found myself amidst an assortment of eager faces, each a reflection of curiosity and wanderlust. There stood the tour guide, Efe, a beacon amidst the sea of anticipation, his presence commanding yet welcoming, much like a seasoned captain before setting sail into uncharted waters. As I stepped into the safari jeep, it felt as if I were boarding a vessel destined for the depths of my soul, embarking on a voyage where the landscapes outside mirrored the unexplored territories within.

The ignition of the engine was the turning of a key, unlocking the gates to a world where the raw beauty of nature and the intricacies of my inner self would intertwine. This journey was not just a passage through the savannah but a dive into the heart of discovery, where the external adventure catalyzed an internal exploration, promising revelations at every turn.

As our safari jeep meandered through the untamed heart of the savannah, the air was alive with the spirit of adventure. The landscape unfurled before us like a canvas painted with broad strokes of golden grasses, punctuated by the dark silhouettes of acacia trees against a sky of boundless blue. The sounds of the wild composed a symphony of roars, trumpets, and calls that resonated with the primal essence of this land. Each encounter, from the regal pride of lions basking under the sun to the vibrantly colored toucans, gliding overhead, added layers of awe and reverence to our experience.

The journey through this exotic ecosystem revealed the marvels of nature in their purest forms, with the formidable bulk of hippos in muddy waters, the elegant stature of giraffes against the horizon, and countless other creatures each playing their role in the circle of life. Yet, amidst this array of wildlife, it was the elephants that held a presence most profound. They moved like the whispered secrets of the earth, with a grace that belied their immense size, their steps a slow dance of might and majesty.

As we came to a stop and exited the jeep, to proceed with the walking portion of the safari, our group, a mixture of wonder and curiosity, watched in silence. Most of the elephant herd began to approach us, drawn by an invisible bond between species. They moved with a deliberate calm, their eyes holding stories of ages past. It was then that our tour guide, with a practiced hand, reached into his backpack to retrieve a single, crisp red apple. Holding it up, he gestured towards a distinguished elephant who held back, observing from a distance with a measured caution in her gaze.

"This," he announced, with a tone of reverence, "is Zuri. She is the matriarch of the herd."

In a world vastly different from the one I knew, where leadership was often a mantle borne by males, Zuri's command was a striking contrast. Her authority was not asserted through force but derived from her very being, serving as a testament to the matriarchal society in which these majestic creatures thrived. As the tour guide offered the apple, as an emblem of trust, Zuri's initial hesitation faded. Slowly, with a dignity that seemed to cover her, she approached. It was a moment where time seemed to pause, a bridge built between the worlds of human and elephant.

While we watched this interaction, the tour guide shared, "Zuri has seen more of life's harsh realities than any creature should. She witnessed her mother's demise at the hands of poachers, eager for ivory. As you can see, by looking at her left ear, she did not escape unscathed."

His voice carried a weight of sadness, a lament for the injustices inflicted upon these gentle giants. The group fell silent, each of us processing the gravity of Zuri's story. It was a poignant reminder of the vulnerability that came with beauty and strength, of the greed that often shadows innocence. As Zuri accepted the apple, her trunk gently wrapped around it, with an unspoken understanding and recognition of her resilience as well as a silent vow of respect from us, the onlookers.

In this encounter, beneath the vast African sky, amid the whispers of the grass and the tales of survival and loss, we found a connection. It was a moment that transcended the boundaries of species, a testament to the enduring spirit of life in the face of adversity. And as Zuri, with her guarded trust now slightly subsided, merged back with her herd, we were left with a deeper appreciation for the wild, a profound respect for its inhabitants, and a lingering question about the true cost of humanity's desires.

As Zuri rejoined her herd, our eyes remained locked, creating an invisible link between us. It was as if she could sense the shadows of pain that lingered within me, reflecting her own experiences of loss and resilience. In her gaze, I saw not just her narrative but also my own as a reflection of adversity, endurance, and the quiet fortitude born from facing life's challenges head-on.

As the tour group began to move ahead, a pull from within led me to linger, my steps unconsciously guiding me closer to the magnificent gentle giants that roamed these lands with grace and poise. It was that moment that felt suspended outside of time. Zuri, whose eyes were deep pools of wisdom, remained locked with mine with an intensity that seemed to pierce through the veils of our distinct existences. There was a recognition, a silent understanding that transcended the need for spoken words, bridging our worlds with the invisible fibers of shared experience and unvoiced sorrow.

This silent exchange, devoid of words yet full of meaning, felt like a communion of souls. Zuri's silent acknowledgment of our shared pain struck a sense of peace that permeated so deep it felt as though the weight of my worries had been momentarily lifted. Surrounded by the endless expanse of the savannah, under the watchful gaze of this wise matriarch, I found a moment of solace and a brief interval where the complexities of life seemed to simplify. I was introduced to the universal bonds of understanding and empathy that link all sentient beings.

Almost without hesitation, I allowed the tour group to continue on as I drifted in the opposite direction, gently approaching the herd. As they began to continue their migration, I followed and began to walk side by side with Zuri, maintaining a safe and unthreatening distance. At this point I had released any concern of the tour group leaving me behind.

I traveled all the way to the other side of the world, to unlock the next version of myself and I wasn't going to allow fear of any kind deter me from doing just that. With the rest of the herd following behind us and my tour group disappearing in the distance, I came to the realization that Zuri is the leader because the others trust her sense of direction and decision-making.

Elephants live in fission-fusion societies, where individuals and other herds join and separate from the herd as they see fit. Every member of the herd understood the importance of following wisdom and learning from their leader because many would eventually become leaders of their own herds.

I too felt a magnetic pull towards her, as if an invisible thread connected us across the vast expanse of the savannah. Together, we moved as one, our footsteps echoing in harmony with the rhythm of the earth. With each stride, I felt a deepening connection to the natural world around me, a sense of belonging that transcended the boundaries of language and culture. In the silent exchange of glances, I saw reflected in Zuri's eyes the wisdom of ages, the resilience of spirit, and the innate understanding of life's mysteries. It was as if she held the key to unlock the deepest truths of existence, inviting me to explore the depths of my own soul in her presence.

As time continued to pass, I continued along with no knowledge of where I was following these majestic creatures to. This was the first time that I deliberately traveled for hours with no plan, map, or even real concern. The ambient silence, outside of the powerful steps being taken across the land, allowed me to get lost in thought, without the loud distractions of the world.

As the sun began its descent towards the horizon, casting

long shadows across the savannah, the peaceful silence was interrupted by the sound of drums and laughter in the distance. I had also realized that I had no clue where I was nor how I was going to find my way back to where I came from. With a sense of careless spontaneity, I continued on as we ventured closer to the sounds illuminating the air.

The village that loomed on the horizon seemed to beckon with the promise of warmth and hospitality, yet I couldn't shake the twinge of nervousness that gnawed at my stomach. Would they welcome an outsider like me into their midst?

As we drew nearer, the laughter of children dancing in the dusty streets filled the air, their joy infectious and their smiles radiant. With each step, my apprehension melted away and was replaced by a sense of wonder and curiosity at the vibrant exhibit of life unfolding before me. And then, amidst the multitude of joyful faces, I saw a familiar figure emerging from the crowd. It was Efe, the tour guide from earlier, his face alight with recognition and gratitude.

As he approached, he and the village elder, greeted Zuri with reverence, acknowledging her role in guiding me safely to the village. In that moment, I realized the depth of Zuri's wisdom and compassion. She had brought me here not out of mere chance, but with the purpose of ensuring my safety and well-being as night descended upon the savannah. With a heart full of gratitude, I followed Efe into the heart of the village, welcomed by open arms and warm smiles.

The night covered the village, adorned with a tapestry of stars. The air was alive with the heartbeat of drums, the symphony of laughter mingling with the spicy scent wafting from the cooking fires. In this twilight, life was not just observed but felt with every sense. Drawn into the revelry, I found myself swept up in the joyous celebration, dancing with the children beneath the canopy of stars, my heart overflowing with a sense of belonging.

As the night wore on, I joined Zuri, seated under the sprawling branches of a towering apple tree, displaying a meager number of apples, gnarled roots reaching deep into the earth, and its branches stretching towards the heavens. The village elder, a figure of quiet wisdom and grace, also joined us, his eyes twinkling with the light of a thousand stories.

We spoke of our respective cultures, exchanging tales of tradition and heritage, of the bonds that unite us as human beings despite our differences. With each word, I felt a silent bond forming between us, forged in the fires of mutual understanding and respect.

"Ajani," he began, "I see the weight of the world in your eyes. Tell me, why do you burden yourself with this overbearing weight?"

I sighed, feeling the rawness of truths I had long buried. "I was raised in a society where worth is measured by the number of commas in your bank account as well as the gleam and abundance of one's possessions. These things, I thought, were symbols of success, proof that I had risen above my challenging childhood, my father's doubts, and my mother's quiet despair. In my country, we are all trained to pursue this 'American Dream,' and somewhere along the journey, it began to feel more like a beautiful nightmare. I have been blessed enough to live out all of my childhood fantasies, to include things like making an abundance of money, owning a luxury home, owning multiple dream cars, and laying with some of the most beautiful women in the world. I always believed that these things would lead to my 'happily ever after' life, but I'm starting to feel like they don't, even in the slightest."

The elder nodded with a grin, his gaze never leaving the tree. "The apple tree," he gestured, "does not boast of its bounty nor does it need adornment to fulfill its purpose. It stands in its truth, providing sustenance and shelter. It's worth, undeniable, lies in its being, not in its appearance. Ajani, can a man not be like the apple tree, his worth intrinsic and his life full of purpose without the excess? It is the nature of man to toil for the sand when it is the sea that calls to his soul. You seek women to fill your bed and warm your body, forgetting it is your spirit that shivers in the cold of transient spiritual connections. You see, the pursuit of material wealth can either be a journey towards comfort and security or a flight from the fear of scarcity. But in excess, it becomes a chain that weighs down the spirit. A home with more rooms than warmth, vehicles that transport an empty heart—these are not symbols of success, but markers of a journey misplaced. For the oasis of life is found in moments of connection, in the wealth of our shared gifts, in the richness of a heartfelt gesture."

I felt the truth of these words resonate within me, a calling to a more purpose-driven life. "And how do we ensure we don't fall into greed's subtle trap?" I asked, a student eager for the lesson.

"By understanding the cyclical nature of life," the elder replied. "A tree bears fruit, which falls and feeds the earth, which, in turn, nourishes the tree. Wealth, when hoarded, stagnates. But when circulated with good intent, it fosters growth everywhere."

I absorbed the words, their truth resonating with a clarity that startled me. I had chased these symbols, believing they were the destination rather than the scenery along the path. Maybe I had begin to fall victim to a sense of greed. Now, engulfed in my reflective thoughts, I began to wonder, to myself "why?"

As I pondered, a breeze stirred, whispering secrets through the leaves. My upbringing has been a fortress, and within its walls, trust is a currency seldom earned and easily spent. I innately placed my trust in those I loved and who loved me. What is love, but a desert mirage to a heart that fears the mirage may never become the sea?

"Trust," I whispered, a fragile word that hung in the balmy air, "I've built walls around my heart, fearing it might shatter against the rocks of betrayal, as it did in my youth."

Then, I continued to verbalize the present thoughts from my mind. "Those material things and even the beautiful women who have laid in my bed were for validation and strokes to my own ego. The pleasure was temporary and after it faded, the desire for more immediately arose, but I guess I never asked myself why."

The elder's eyes, reflecting the wisdom of the tree we sat beneath, were gentle. "Trust," he imparted, "is the seed from which relationships grow. Yet like all living things, it must be nurtured and sometimes pruned. Your past has taught you caution, and that is a valuable lesson, but let it not teach you fear. For just as Ola, here, sheds her leaves to grow anew, so must you shed your fears to let trust take root once more. That trust must begin within."

A silence settled between us, rich with unspoken understanding. The elder continued, "Intimate relationships— they are gardens of their own kind. They require patience, labor, and most of all, the courage to see the beauty in imperfection. To love another is to accept the seasonality of the human heart, knowing that just as the tree endures storms to bask again in sunlight, so does true commitment withstand the tempests of doubt and misunderstanding. Love is not the mirage, my young friend; it is the very sea you yearn for. But it asks that you sail its depths, not just admire it from the shore."

I felt a weight begin to lift with the elder's words, as if the stars themselves conspired to unlock the long-closed chambers of my heart. "And how does one balance this pursuit of material comfort with the longing for spiritual fulfillment?" I asked, as a seeker yearning for enlightenment.

The elder smiled. "The idea of balance is found in gratitude for the present, ambition for the future, and wisdom from the past. It's understanding that material comfort can warm the body but only a fulfilled spirit can warm the soul. There is no thread that does not serve its purpose. The material is but the vessel that carries the essence of life; it is empty without the spirit. Enjoy the fruits of your labor, but do not let them anchor you to the shallows occupied by much of the modern-day world. For a man's soul is born of the boundless seas, and it is there it must return."

As the fireflies began their nocturnal dance, the elder's words took root in my mind. "The most profound 'why'," the elder concluded, "is the one that leads you to the essence of your being. Live with the simplicity of the apple tree, which asks not for gold nor grandeur, but thrives in its divine purpose of being. Let your life be a journey that enriches not just your pockets, but also the pockets of others' souls."

The moon climbed higher, bathing the village in a silver glow as the elder continued to impart his wisdom upon me, as Zuri rested against Ola's immense trunk.

"Remember, Ajani, live a life rich in spirit, build relationships on the foundation of mutual growth, and measure success not by what you gather, but by what you scatter, such as the love, the kindness, and the wisdom you share."

In the elder's presence, under the wise old apple tree, I found the beginnings of a path laid with more than the gold of this world, but with the light of understanding, leading me towards a dawn of transformation. As the rest of the village fell into a restful slumber, I sat, a man amidst the transformation I had traveled to this region of the world to discover. The whispers of the tree and the echoes of ancient wisdom were charting a new course for my life; one paved with the riches of the soul, that promised the true alchemy of life. My heart absorbed every word of the wise elder with the truth of them resonating within me, yet I yearned for so much more.

"And what are your thoughts of those who betray us?" I asked, the memory of my former business partner still a sharp sting.

"Betrayal is the tool with which life chisels us into stronger beings," the elder spoke gently. "It teaches us to be wise but also reminds us that even in pain, there's a lesson of strength and forgiveness. Yes, your former associates stole from you, but do not neglect what they provided you with in return."

I then thought of my former business associates, who I had once considered friends, not with resentment, but with a sort of melancholic gratitude. They had indeed, unwittingly, sent me on this quest, which taught me the importance of discernment and also became a journey that pushed me to confront the deeper meaning of life and my purpose within it.

"I've seen wealth amassed, and I've witnessed it vanish like mist," the elder continued, his eyes reflecting the moonlight. "Yet, it's the unseen growth, the intangible wealth of experience and knowledge, that seems to endure."

"The tree you sit under," the elder began, "grows strong because its roots are deep, unseen. It shares its gifts freely, without want for reward. You have garnered much, Ajani, but remember, what nourishes us most are the gifts we give, not the riches we accumulate. Remember, a tree does not drink its own nectar nor feast on its fruits. Your gifts are not solely for your consumption. They're for the world, to heal, to inspire, to uplift. The more you give, the richer you become."

A quiet understanding settled between us, the wisdom of ages passing through the elder's words, seeping into my consciousness.

I pondered for a moment, "So, why do some gather wealth with ease, while others, equally deserving, find only hardship?"

The elder picked a leaf from the ground, examining its veins like one would a map. "Success, my son, is much like a raincloud," he explained. "It may pour over one patch of land and not another. Some seeds will flourish while others won't, no matter their potential. What matters is the richness of the soil of your spirit, your intent, and actions."

As we entered into the midnight hours, the elder stood, his figure casting a long shadow in the firelight. "Stay with us, Ajani. Learn our ways, the rhythms of our life. Let the simplicity of our existence teach you the complexity of living fully."

Fill with a warm sense of belonging, I accepted, realizing the village was not just a place but a state of being, a new chapter of growth, much like the mighty tree under which we conversed. This was an exchange with the world, a dance of give and take, and a balance of holding on and letting go.

The weeks turned into months, and the man that I was, began to morph into the man I am now. The anger and betrayal transformed into lessons of forgiveness and strength. The relentless pursuit of more became a journey towards depth and meaning. The external validations I sought became less important than the internal affirmations I was beginning to cultivate. As the end of my self-imposed sabbatical neared, I knew I would return home changed. The businesses would still demand my attention, the hustle of city life would beckon with open arms, but I would step back into that world with a new armor, woven with threads of self-awareness, compassion, and true purpose.

The 'why' of my existence had shifted from a focus on success to a focus on significance. I would continue to build, to create, to lead, but with a foundation rooted in the lessons learned from this land and its people, and from the silent conversations with the stars. My last night before the journey back was filled with a reflective quiet. The journal lay open on my lap, the pages a testimony to the transformation that had occurred. The words I had written were not just a recount of time and experiences, but a map of my inner landscape, charting the path from who I was to who I am becoming.

The answer to "Why am I here?" had become clear. I was here because this was where I was meant to be—physically, emotionally, spiritually. I was here because every choice, every challenge, every triumph, and every failure had led me to this moment of profound clarity. I was here to learn that life's truest success isn't the sum of what you have but the essence of who you become. And as I closed my journal and looked out into the night, I felt a deep connection to everything that is, was, and will be. I was ready to go home, to bring back with me the gifts of this journey, not just the souvenirs for my shelves, but the lessons for my soul.

In the quiet before dawn, as the first light began to touch the horizon, I packed my bags. I was not leaving this place; I was taking the seeds from it, with me, carrying its essence in the core of my being. My journey was far from over; in many ways, it was just beginning. But as the sun rose, casting its first warm rays on the land that had been my refuge, I stepped forward with a heart full of gratitude, eyes wide open, and a spirit renewed.

I was here because my new journey had only just begun.

4 THE VICTOR

As I sat, mentally rejuvenated and spiritually woke, in seat A1, ready for takeoff back to my home, my mind delved into the depths of my initial eternal question: Why? Why don't we ask why? Why do we do the things we do? Why do we believe in the things we believe in? Why do we interact with other entities the way that we do? I believe this freeing journey began to unlock the answers to these questions, which were critical to having a true understanding of self. Do we naturally do, believe, and interact the way that we do, or are these character traits influenced by outside entities? That leads me to ask, are humans born good, evil, or amoral? This question has plagued philosophers and thinkers for centuries, and after this life-changing trip to the Motherland, it haunted my thoughts as well.

Throughout my travel experiences, I have been exposed to customs, views, and energies that forced me to begin dissecting the why within every aspect of my 33 years of existence on this earth. As we gracefully glided through the clouds, I allowed my mind to wander freely, dissecting the newfound answers, which stretched far beyond the confines of societal norms.

I contemplated the notion that perhaps we are born as blank slates, innocent and untainted by the world's complexities.

41

Could it be that morality is a construct imposed upon us by external forces rather than an inherent quality? My journey into the realm of human nature began with the exploration of my own existence. I pondered the moments of my earliest consciousness, the beginning of my moral compass. I was once an innocent being, devoid of biases or judgments, pure in my thoughts and intentions. In that state of innocence, I possessed no preconceived notions of good or evil. My moral slate was blank, waiting to be written upon by the experiences and influences that would shape me.

Now, after being exposed to various cultures, I have come to understand that my moral development was not solely a product of my own nature but was also influenced by the beliefs and values of those around me. I couldn't help but wonder to myself, "Why is this not a more prevalent topic of discussion?"

Then I quickly remembered that a large piece of the population is too busy arguing about dating issues, get-rich-quick schemes, and how many new genders there are. Then it hit me; the small group controls the large group by keeping them entertained with nonsense, so they have no time to see nor seek the truth, which would inherently set them free. I was once a part of that large group as well, so how did I escape it? In order to determine that, I have to start from the origin and revisit all of my experiences, traumas, and triumphs to understand how I got to this level of consciousness.

In the face of uncertainty, I stand tall, my heart ablaze with the fire of purpose. The journey I have embarked upon has led me to this pivotal moment, where the path ahead is unveiled before me. The echoes of my past whisper in the depths of my being, reminding me of the hurdles I have overcome and the strength that lies within. As I gaze upon the crossroads of my life, I am humbled by the transformative power of my journey. The external variants that once threatened to derail me have now become stepping stones, guiding me closer to the truth that resides within. The illusions that once clouded my vision have dissipated, revealing the essence of my divine purpose. With every step I take, I am reminded that this path is uniquely mine to walk. It is not a journey defined by the expectations of others or the confines of societal norms. It is a quest for authenticity, a relentless pursuit of truth and self-discovery. I have come to realize that my purpose is not an external destination to be reached but a state of being to be embodied.

The world around me teems with distractions and temptations, pulling me away from my true calling. The allure of superficial success and the pursuit of empty validations beckon, but I must remain steadfast in my commitment to stay true to myself. I refuse to ever again compromise my authenticity for the sake of external gratification. In the depths of my being, I carry the unwavering belief that my purpose extends beyond my own individual journey. I understand the interconnectedness of all beings and embrace the responsibility to uplift and inspire those around me. As I walk this path, I seek to ignite the flame of purpose in others, encouraging them to question the narratives that confine them and uncover their own divine potential.

There are times when the road ahead appears shrouded in darkness, and doubt creeps into the corners of my mind. But I am fortified by the knowledge that the challenges I face are not meant to break me but to mold me into a stronger, more resilient version of myself. I draw strength from the lessons I have learned, from the depths of my own healing and growth. As I move forward, I am guided by a burning desire to be the father I wished I had, to break the cycles of the past and create a legacy of love, compassion, and purpose. I yearn to provide a foundation of stability and support, to be a beacon of light for those who walk alongside me. The path unfolds before me, winding through the peaks and valleys of life's tapestry. I am prepared for the challenges that lie ahead, knowing that each obstacle is an opportunity for growth. I trust in the divine timing of the universe, knowing that every twist and turn is leading me closer to the fulfillment of my purpose.

In this moment, I am filled with gratitude for the journey I have undertaken. The weight of my shadows has become a testament to my resilience, and the wounds of my past have become the wellspring of my compassion. I embrace the call of my purpose, knowing that it is not a destination to be reached but a lifelong dance of self-discovery and growth.

As I sit, seat reclined, taking a sip of this fine beverage, perfectly curated by the first-class stewardess, I can't help but to replay the words of the village elder, "Live with the simplicity of the apple tree, which asks not for gold nor grandeur but thrives in its divine purpose of being." There will be a tidal wave of tasks, demands, and responsibilities once I land and set foot back on my home soil, but in this moment, I am going to clear my mind, relish in this present moment, and just be.

PART II: ZURI

Zuri
Origin: Swahili, Eastern African
Meaning: Beautiful

5 WHO IS ZURI?

In the nurturing cradle of the savannah, amidst a symphony of life that hummed beneath the vast African sky, Zuri's story began. At birth, her legs, though wobbly, bore her weight as she stood, serving as a testament to the resilience etched into her being. Her first steps were shaky, but necessary, binding her to the safety of the herd and the watchful eye of her mother. This was her first dance with destiny, one that tethered her to the earth's ancient rhythm.

Her skin was a map of the earth's textures, a patchwork of wrinkles yet to be etched by the passage of time. The world around her was a symphony of sounds and sensations, melodies of elephant rumbles and the whisper of the savannah grass. These vibrations, felt through delicate feet and keen ears, were the language of the giants, and Zuri absorbed them, an eager student of the wild's unspoken words. Though her sight was temporarily limited, her long eyelashes fluttered like the delicate wings of a butterfly, sensing the world in soft shades and movements.

Zuri was born with an instinctual connection to the earth. Her trunk, initially clumsy and unwieldly, was a remarkable appendage endowed with around 40,000 muscles. As days unfurled into weeks, Zuri's trunk began to find its purpose, exploring and experimenting, touching, and grasping. It was an extension of her very soul, growing in dexterity, becoming an instrument of communication, an appendage for comfort, and a tool for discovery.

Zuri's mother, the herd's matriarch, as well as the other elders were her first guides, her protectors, and her educators. From them, Zuri learned the art of being. They imparted lessons that were ingrained in their collective memory, to include how to forage, how to bathe in the dust and water, and how to greet one another in their society of giants. They encircled Zuri with love, a protective barrier against the predators and the elements.

In her early days, Zuri observed, imitated, and stumbled through her lessons, each mistake a stone upon which to build her knowledge. Her mother's guidance was as vital as the milk that nourished her. It was from her that Zuri learned the nuances of elephant communication through the trumpets, rumbles, and roars that could convey joy, anger, or distress. Her mother taught her how to interpret the low-frequency messages that vibrated through the ground as seismic whispers that relayed messages over vast distances.

The savannah was not just a home, but a classroom. Every tree, waterhole, and plain held lessons on survival and existence. The matriarchs led the herd on ancient migratory routes, passing down the wisdom of generations. They showed Zuri the paths woven through the land by the footsteps of her ancestors, the secret havens where water was plenty, and the danger zones where shadows moved with lethal intent.

Zuri's emotional education was equally rich in experience. The herd showed her empathy, often tenderly touching each other with their trunks, a comfort that spoke without words. They demonstrated cooperation, working together to ward off threats and support the calves and the elderly. Through play and interaction, Zuri began to understand her place within this complex assortment of relationships among earth's other inhabitants.

In the heart of the savannah, where the sky stretches endlessly and the golden grass whispers tales of ancient times, there existed a harmony among the creatures that called this expanse home. Zuri, young and spirited, was one of them, cradled in the safety and wisdom of her herd. But beneath the serene surface of their world, a threat lurked, one that carried the stench of greed and the sound of destruction.

It was on a day that had started like any other, with the sun rising grandly as if painting the sky with strokes of crimson and gold, that the herd sensed the danger before it appeared, a tension in the air, a disturbance on the wind. Zuri's mother, the matriarch, with her tusks that told stories of decades lived and battles won, led the herd with a commanding presence that had always been their shield. But no amount of strength or foresight could have prepared them for the devastation that descended upon them that day. The calamity was not from the skies nor the earth, but from an outside presence, brought by humans whose hearts were darkened by greed. These poachers, as they were known, invaded the paradise of the savannah with a thunderous fury that ripped through the air like a storm of malice.

As the poachers closed in, their vehicles churning up the earth, their guns a death knell, the herd rallied around Zuri and the other calfs. They encircled them with a fortress of flesh and bone. Their massive forms were a barricade against the chaos. Zuri's mother, a towering figure of matriarchal might, used her body to shield her calf, pushing Zuri deeper into the brush, her eyes locking with her daughter's in a silent plea to stay hidden, to stay silent.

The sound of gunfire tore through the fabric of the savannah, a symphony of terror that drowned out the calls of the wild. The herd was in disarray, their formations broken by the invasion, their unity tested as they scattered in a desperate bid for survival. Zuri, trembling in the underbrush, could do nothing but watch as the scene unfolded with a brutality that would be etched into her memory forever.

Her mother, once unmovable, became the target of the poachers' insatiable lust for ivory. They were relentless, ganging up on her, their bullets a hailstorm that seemed to never cease. The matriarch, wounded and valiant, fought with the fury of a mother protecting her young, her roars were a mix of rage and pain that resonated across the plains.

In the end, the savannah fell silent, the dust settled, and Zuri emerged from her hiding place, wounded by a stray bullet, and the world as she knew it irrevocably altered. Her mother lay still, a giant felled, her life extinguished by the hands of greed. The herd, leaderless and heartbroken, fragmented in the wake of the loss.

Some members, paralyzed by fear, wandered aimlessly. Others rallied in small groups, looking for direction in a world that suddenly seemed vast and unfamiliar. Zuri stood among them, with a bullet-pierced left ear, motherless, and adrift. The matriarch's wisdom had been a guiding star. Her strength was the foundation upon which the herd had thrived. Now, they were cast into a night of uncertainty, the guiding star extinguished, the foundation crumbled.

The herd splintered with each fragment serving as a stark reminder of the unity they once shared. Elders, once companions under the matriarch's leadership, now stepped forward to guide those who would follow them. The choice that lay before Zuri was one weighted with the legacy of her mother's leadership and the pain of her absence.

Zuri, still young but marked by the indelible experience of loss and survival, faced the decision of whom to follow. It was a choice that bore not just the question of survival but of identity.

Each potential leader offered a different path, a different way of navigating the savannah's vastness and dangers. To choose was to step forward into a future unwritten, to carry the legacy of her mother in a world that had shown its harshest face.

As the days passed and the pain of her mother's loss turned from a sharp sting to a deep ache, Zuri's path began to sway. A fierce resolve took root within her, a resolve to challenge the humans who dared to shatter the sanctity of their lives. Where there was once a naïve trust, a deep-seated suspicion of all humans took root. Each human scent on the wind was a call to retribution, and she became a silent guardian of her kind, her eyes always seeking the peril of men. The desire for revenge simmered within her like a dormant volcano, biding its time, awaiting a sign.

She would not succumb to the bitterness of vengeance, for to do so would be to lose herself and the wisdom her mother had instilled in her. She would honor the memory of the fallen matriarch not with violence but by living with the strength, compassion, and leadership that had been her mother's greatest gifts.

In the wake of tragedy, Zuri found what she believed to be her purpose. She would learn to lead, not with the might of her tusks but with the depth of her understanding. She would protect, not through the ferocity of her charge but with the range of her empathy. And in the silence left by her mother's passing, Zuri would echo the teachings that would shape the future of her herd.

She chose to follow an elder, one who had walked in step with her mother, whose wisdom was etched in the lines of her face and whose steps spoke of a lifetime treading the savannah's paths. This elder, who had known Zuri since her birth, now became her mentor, her guide in a journey that was just beginning.

As Zuri grew under the tutelage of the elder, the memories of her mother's teachings melded with the lessons learned from her new leader. Her tragedy became a source of silent fortitude. Each day was a testament to her resilience; each decision she made reflected her mother's enduring spirit.

The savannah continued to speak to Zuri, though now its voice was tinged with a somber hue. She learned the ways of the earth with a passion born of loss, embracing her heritage with every step she took. She memorized the twists and turns of the rivers, the whisper of the grasses that told of rain, the distant rumble that warned of approaching herds or humans.

The herd, though fragmented, remained her family, and Zuri found her place among them. Her presence brought comfort to the others, her resolve a beacon in the unsteady times that followed. She became a pillar, a young but immovable force that helped to anchor the others who were adrift in their mourning.

As Zuri grew, the dichotomy of divine nature and external influence began to shape her. She was of the earth's pulse, its rhythm, and its ancient knowledge. Yet, she was also touched by the darkness of human greed and violence, which left scars, both visible and not visible, that the savannah's gentle hands struggled to heal. These outside forces challenged her, forcing the herd to adapt, to be cautious, and in Zuri's case, to harbor burning resentment.

As years pass, Zuri, now a young matriarch, was faced with the challenges of leadership. She bore the responsibility of guiding her herd through the labyrinth of life where the threat of predators, both animal and human, lurked behind the facade of nature's serenity. It was a role she took on with pride, her mother's absence, a constant reminder of her newfound purpose in life.

Zuri's tenure as matriarch saw her flourishing in her role, her wisdom and strength becoming the bedrock for her herd's survival and prosperity. Under her vigilant leadership, they navigated the vast savannah with grace, avoiding natural predators and finding the best grazing grounds through the changing seasons. Her deep understanding of the land and its hidden dangers, combined with her decisive actions, fostered a period of peace and stability.

The herd thrived, their numbers growing as they welcomed new calves into the fold, each birth celebrated as a triumph of life over the lurking shadows of the wilderness. Zuri, standing tall amidst her family, felt a profound sense of accomplishment and connection. For a time, it seemed as though they were untouchable, as if the vast plains they roamed were theirs alone, a kingdom where she reigned with gentle authority. This golden period was a testament to her success, filling her heart with pride and a hopeful vision for the future.

Then came the day where the savannah, usually a symphony of life, was abruptly silenced by a harsh and deadly encounter with poachers, once again. This event, much like the one that claimed the life of Zuri's mother, years prior, unfolded rapidly as dusk merged day with night, casting long shadows that masked the danger lurking at the edges of visibility.

A group of poachers, driven by a ruthless greed, ambushed the herd, their guns shattering the tranquility of the wilderness. The attack was brutal and swift, leaving one of Zuri's herd members lifeless in the dust, her fall marking the ground with a stark reminder of the cruelty inflicted upon their kind.

This tragedy fractured the once-unified spirit of the herd. Zuri, blindsided by the assault, was consumed by guilt and self-doubt. She tormented herself with thoughts of what signs she might have missed, agonizing over her perceived failure to protect her family. The cohesion of the herd suffered; fear and uncertainty crept in, causing some members to splinter off, preferring the chances of survival on their own rather than under the leadership they no longer trusted implicitly. This departure was a painful blow to Zuri, deepening her sense of isolation and questioning her role as the matriarch.

Amidst this upheaval, Zuri's leadership was both challenged and crucial. She wrestled with her own vulnerabilities while striving to muster the strength that the remainder of her herd needed to navigate through their collective grief and disrupted safety. Her role as a leader had never felt more daunting, each decision weighed down by the acute awareness of its potential life-or-death consequences. The savannah no longer just spoke of natural rhythms and ancient paths but whispered warnings of the dangers that stalked them by both day and night.

As the shadows lengthen over the savannah, casting the memories of loss in stark relief against the backdrop of survival, the story of Zuri continues. Her journey of rediscovery and the quest to reaffirm her purpose is more crucial now than ever. Facing her darkest moments, Zuri must navigate through the tumult of emotions and the fragmented trust of her herd. Will she rise, fortified by the trials, to lead her family to safer pastures? Or will the weight of her responsibilities and the ghosts of past losses drive her to seek a new understanding of her role within the vast, whispering wilderness?

Join Zuri as she delves deeper into the essence of her being, exploring the very fibers of her spirit and leadership in a world that is unforgiving yet rich with the promise of renewal. Her story is one of resilience and rebirth, a compelling call to journey with her as she discovers the paths that will lead not only to her own salvation but to the enduring legacy she aims to build amidst the ever-changing cycles of life.

6 WHY ARE THINGS THIS WAY?

Our lives are a symphony of silent conversations, a dance of subtle gestures and deep rumbles that resonate through the ground, carrying messages of caution, of camaraderie, and of communal gatherings. My role is not just to lead but to communicate, to ensure the safety and unity of our family against the backdrop of nature's opulence and its dangers. Recently, this duty has been tested; we suffered a brutal encounter with poachers that cost us one of our own. The herd is rattled, and I am laden with a heavy sorrow, mourning the loss while constantly vigilant against further threats.

The life of an elephant is woven with the threads of connection, our existence a delicate balance between the abundance the land offers and the dangers it conceals. With each step, I guide my herd through the labyrinth of the savannah, our paths marked by the silent exchanges between us. We speak in a language born of the earth, a dialogue of low-frequency calls that can travel over vast distances, invisible yet palpable threads that bind us together. This is how we warn each other of lurking predators hidden by the grasses or share the location of water holes in the often arid atmosphere of the land. Our gatherings are also orchestrated through these silent calls, a summoning of families and friends to converge at ancient meeting spots that have witnessed the passage of countless generations.

Here, under the wide expanse of the sky, we celebrate the ties that bind us, the collective memory of our kind that stretches back through time. These meetings are a testament to our social nature, to the deep bonds of kinship and friendship that define our existence as much as the need for sustenance and shelter.

To understand our lives is to glimpse into a world where communication transcends words, where the land itself is a living entity that speaks to those who know how to listen. It is a life of complexity and simplicity, of traversing the vastness of the savannah with the grace of beings who carry the wisdom of the ages in their steps. As matriarch, my voice serves as the guide that steers my herd through the dance of survival and unity, a beacon that shines amidst the challenges and the beauty of our shared journey.

My memory, like a library written in the sands of time, where every footprint tells a story, still holds the shadows of loss, which loom large over my existence. In the aftermath of my mother's death, a fortress rose around my heart, stone by stone, each one a testament to the betrayal that had severed the innocence of my trust. My steps became cautious, each one measured, as I led my herd through the labyrinth of life.

As I grappled with the fresh wounds inflicted by the recent poacher attack, a tsunami of emotions surged through me, each wave crashing harder than the last. My heart, already fortified against the harsh realities of the wild, now bore the added weight of grief and guilt. How could I have let this happen? The question gnawed at me relentlessly, the weight of my responsibility as matriarch feeling more burdensome than ever. The loss of a life I was sworn to protect, left a void that echoed painfully in my every thought and step. The betrayal of humanity, once again, tarnished the landscape of my trust, deepening the shadows that lingered from my past.

In these moments of deep reflection and sorrow, I realized that to lead is not just to guide but also to learn and adapt from every misstep and tragedy. The path to recovery seemed daunting, yet necessary. I knew I needed to replenish my spirit, to rekindle the drive that had propelled me forward thus far.

The world had once again proven its cruelty, but I could not let it define us or our future. To heal, to rebuild what was lost, I turned to the wisdom of the land and the quiet resilience that had always guided us. It was time for a change. Drawing from the energy of the earth, the soft murmur of the streams, and the rustling of the leaves, I began to piece together my fractured spirit. This connection to nature, which had always soothed and sustained us, now served as my refuge and my source of strength.

I vowed to rise from this adversity with a renewed vigor, to lead my herd not just through survival, but towards a life where joy could once again take root amidst the vast savannah. This journey of healing was not just for me, but for every member of my herd, as we sought to reclaim the peace that was so brutally snatched from us.

Despite the barricade around my heart, fragments of a tender past and unbridled joy and innocence, beckon me with the allure of sweet memories. It was the reflection of these sweet memories that led me to a faraway land that my mother introduced me to when I was just a few weeks old, when the world seemed vast and kind. This nostalgia drew me and my herd to the migration, leading to the edges of a remote village, where the abundance of nature offered itself freely, hanging from the branches of plentiful trees.

As we embarked on the weeks-long journey to the remote village, each day's trek brought with it a chance for contemplation and conversation that seemed to heal the wounds of our recent ordeal. I walked at the forefront, feeling the ancient rhythms of the land underfoot, guiding my herd through paths both new and old. During the cooler hours of dusk, as we settled beneath the expansive sky, the younger elephants would gather around, their eyes wide with the promise of new experiences.

One evening, by the light of a particularly bright moon, one of the younger females, approached me. Her vibration was soft but filled with the curiosity that thrived despite our hardships. "Zuri," she began, hesitant yet eager, "what do you think awaits us at this village you speak of so fondly? Will it be a place where we can forget the shadows that follow us?"

I paused, considering her concerns, the weight of my leadership ever-present. "Sweetheart, the village holds memories of peace and simplicity," I replied, my demeanor firm with the hope I had worked to cultivate. "It is a place where the land speaks in gentle whispers and the trees offer their bounty freely. We go there not to forget our past but to remember that amidst the vastness of this world, there are still sanctuaries untouched by the chaos we've known. This journey, long as it may be, is our path to rediscover the light that hardship can obscure."

As we continued our nightly discussions, these exchanges became a tapestry of shared hopes and lingering fears, woven under starlit skies. With each story shared, the bonds within our herd strengthened, and I felt a gradual shift within me. This migration was not just a physical relocation; it was a pilgrimage towards healing, understanding, and perhaps, redemption. The act of moving forward, step by step, seemed to slowly rebuild the trust that had been shattered, and I found solace in the collective resilience of my herd.

As dawn crept upon us, with the soft blush of sunlight beginning to streak across the horizon, we neared our sacred destination. The air grew richer with the scent of blooming flowers and fresh earth was a clear signal that we were close. Our pace quickened, driven by an unspoken anticipation that fluttered through the herd like a gentle breeze. The youngest of our group pranced playfully, their spirits uplifted by the nearing change in scenery, while the elders moved with a dignified grace, embodying the wisdom of countless journeys.

Just as the first rays of the sun caressed the earth, painting the world in hues of gold and amber, the silhouette of the village emerged from the mist. It was a sight that breathed new energy into our weary souls. Nestled around this sanctuary was a verdant landscape dotted with apple trees, their boughs heavy with fruit that glimmered like jewels in the morning light.

At first, the sight of these laden trees caused a stir of excitement within the herd, yet our approach was tempered with caution. Each of us, from the smallest calf to the elders, paused to survey the surroundings, our senses sharp and attuned to any sign of danger. Our ears twitched at every rustle, and our trunks sniffed the air for the scent of predators or humans.

As moments passed and no threat presented itself, the tension among us gradually eased. The lush grass beneath our feet and the sweet aroma of ripe apples acted as a balm to our travel-weary spirits. With a collective sense of relief, we began to move forward more freely, our steps growing confident as we ventured closer to the apple trees. The young ones, unable to contain their excitement, trotted ahead, tugging at the low-hanging fruit with their trunks, while the adults kept a watchful eye, ensuring their safety.

The crunch and burst of sweet juices filled the air as we indulged in the apples, each bite more satisfying than the last. It was a feast for the senses, a welcome reward for the long journey we had undertaken. The abundance of food and the serene setting momentarily washed away the hardships of our travels, allowing us to revel in the peace and bounty that the village outskirts offered. This moment of joyous indulgence under the protective gaze of the apple trees was a poignant reminder of the pleasures that life could offer, even after long periods of hardship and vigilance.

As the herd indulged, I glanced into the village square and it was there I first noticed him. With a smile as warm as the morning sun, he silently greeted me from a distance, an acknowledgment of our shared existence. His presence was a curiosity and an anomaly in my cautious world. He seemed to be the only other being present. Still, I watched closely so that my herd could continue to feast without worry.

After a few moments passed, I began to feel small vibrations from the earth that made their way to my feet. It was the vibrations of small footsteps, as other villagers seemingly began to rise from their night slumber. As a result, I motioned to the herd that it was time to move on.

Guided by an instinctive understanding of survival and exploration, we began to familiarize ourselves with the new terrain that surrounded the village. Our movements were methodical, each step taken with a deep respect for the land that hosted us. As the days unfolded, we roamed further, the vast savannah revealing its secrets through the different scents carried by the wind and the varied textures of the earth beneath our feet. The landscape was a mosaic of thriving ecosystems, each area telling its own story.

On one such exploration, we encountered a neighboring herd. Their leader was a wise old matriarch named Sana who approached with a calm demeanor. Our trunks entwined in greeting, a traditional elephant salute that spoke of mutual respect and peace. Sana shared stories of the land, to include those of hidden waterholes, the best grazing spots, and stories of the seasons and how they shaped their movements. Her deep, rumbling vibration resonated with ancient wisdom, her tone was a blend of advice and anecdotes about coexistence with other species that also called this vast landscape home.

"We find strength not just within our herd, but in the bonds we forge with all of nature's creations," Sana conveyed through soft rumbles. "Just as you are drawn to the apples of your newfound haven, remember, every creature here plays a role in the symphony of the savannah."

Inspired by Sana's words, we continued our explorations, encountering various species such as giraffes towering majestically against the skyline, zebras with their striking stripes that seemed to dazzle under the sun, and even packs of lions, with whom we maintained a respectful distance. Each encounter was a lesson in the delicate balance of the ecosystem and our place within it.

Periodically, we would return to the village, drawn back by the irresistible allure of the apple trees. The apples became more than just a source of nourishment. They symbolized a deeper, spiritual sustenance. Each visit to the village reminded us of the initial peace and acceptance we felt, reinforcing a sense of belonging and community that transcended species. The sweet, crisp apples became a metaphor for the life we were cultivating here.

Then, one morning, as the first light painted the sky and we approached our favorite landmark, he stood beneath one of the apple trees with an offering in his outstretched hand. The sight of him, so vulnerable yet so serene, stirred something within me.

My approach was hesitant, every instinct screaming to retreat, but the kindness in his eyes was a seemingly familiar beacon. Accepting the apple from his hand was more than just an act of taking food; it was the acceptance of an olive branch, the bridging of a rift years in the making. From that day forth, this elderly man became a fixture in our visits. His presence was a symbol of the fragile trust that had begun to blossom between us.

Yet, the shadow of my past experiences with humans loomed large, a constant reminder to tread with caution. Why do I feel this way? Why did one human experience jade my overall perception of their kind as a whole? Do they all possess the same mal intent toward all beings who are different than themselves? Maybe some of these feelings and characteristics just lie dormant in some, where they are active in others, but why? I struggled to understand how the universe constructed these seemingly complex creatures with these inwardly unpredictable behaviors.

As the days grew warmer and our trust deepened, I found solace in the steady gaze of the village elder. His gentle demeanor and consistent kindness began to mend the fences around my heart, piece by piece. Carrying the peace that bloomed from this newfound connection, I led the herd away from the village towards an old watering hole.

The journey unfolded under a silence punctuated only by the soft pad of our footsteps against the earth and the distant, harmonious calls of the wild. Reaching the watering hole felt like stepping into a painting, where the blue sky kissed the water's mirror-like surface. I reached out to a young calf at my side, feeling our spirits connect in the shared silence, "See how all life is connected? The sky, the water, and the earth. We all draw from the same sources of life."

The calf, curious and bright, soaked in the scene, his eyes reflecting the vast expanse. Through our bond, he sensed my thoughts, "Is this why we travel so far, to find places like this?"

"Yes," I conveyed, savoring the cool water. "It's about discovering spaces where we can exist freely and fully. It's in places like these where we remember we are part of something larger."

The elders, standing like stoic sentinels at the water's edge, shared in our exchange, their deep rumbles reverberating through the ground, affirming the lesson. "Zuri has shown us much," one elder imparted through a series of soft grunts and foot stamps. "She teaches us not only to survive but to remember our connection to all things."

Their acknowledgment filled me with a quiet strength. This place, much like the village, had woven itself into our story, offering both a literal and metaphorical reflection of our lives. Here, in the communion of water, earth, and herd, the concept of interconnectedness wasn't just understood, but it was lived.

Around us, life thrived in its delicate balance, from the smallest insect to the largest of us, playing its part in the symphony of existence. In this shared moment of serenity, we were reminded of our place in the world. We were not mere survivors of adversity, but custodians of the lands we roamed. Here, by the water that sustained us, our stories mingled like the ripples on the surface, each one a testament to the enduring spirit of life's interconnected dance.

Thus, as my herd and I were beginning to move on from the watering hole we were occupying, I noticed a man emerged in the distance, guiding a small group of people across the familiar terrain of our new home. The echoes of bygone apprehensions resurfaced within me.

Then a feeling came over me that we had a shared history, woven with moments created between him and my late mother. I began to remember some of their encounters in the days when I was just a young calf. These memories flickered through my mind like distant stars. Despite our aged history, despite the memories of camaraderie shared in the glow of the sun, I kept my distance, watching from the shadows of the acacias that now hovered above me.

As he, with his group following close behind, gingerly crept closer, I noticed a surprised look of familiarity in his eyes. I remained on guard as some other members of the herd ventured in the direction of the seemingly friendly group of humans.

As the group came to a stop, the man slowly reached over his shoulder and into his backpack, causing a flutter of anxiety to ripple through me. What was he reaching for? Was I naively exposing the herd to human danger again? My muscles tensed, prepared for the worst. But then, as his hand reemerged, it was grasping a ruby red apple. A sense of relief fill my soul. After seeing the kindness and remorse in the man's eyes, as he gazed at me, I began to feel as though he had no intentions of bringing forth any harm. Thus, I began to make my way over.

As I approached, recognizing the forest green name tag reading "Efe," on his faded tan shirt, I felt as if history was repeating itself in this moment. I was now accepting this red token of appreciation, taking the same steps that my revered mother once took. As he explained, to the rest of the humans, the small piece of my life story that he was aware of, I scanned among the sea of faces. I was drawn to one of these beings, that had an aura and energy that seemed to seek more than just a fleeting encounter with the wild. His eyes held questions, a yearning for understanding that transcended the typical curiosity of tourists. It was in his gaze that I saw a reflection of my own quest for connection, a mirror to the cautious hope that flickered within my heart.

As the rest of the group of humans continued on their journey, this seemingly unique human, remained among the herd, as if our energies refused to separate.

Then he stated, "My name is Ajani."

The moment Ajani stepped into my realm, it felt as though a fresh chapter of my existence was continuing to unfold before me. This human moved with a grace unfamiliar to me, not marred by the shadows of conquest or harm. His eyes, brimming with queries, seemed to delve deep for comprehension, aiming not to seize but to understand. In his gaze, I saw a reflection of my pain and a silent plea for absolution from the earth and its offspring for the transgressions committed by his people.

Time flowed gently as Ajani, from a respectful distance, walked alongside us as we continued to migrate across the savannah. I noticed him observing us with due respect, and I, in turn, grew to acknowledge his silent vow of peace. He embodied the potential for a rebalanced accord between our worlds. An equilibrium that was once shattered was now flickering with the possibility of mending.

Ajani's reflective serenity nudged a shift in my heart. Maybe, just maybe, the essence of humanity was inherently pure. Perhaps a sacred respect for all life pulsed in some of them, echoing my own reverence. This epiphany set upon me, softening the layers of my bitterness while weaving through the cracks like a delicate thread of cohabitation.

As time passed, twilight approached and being aware of the night's lurking perils, I was reminded that Ajani was here in the wild alone with us. He didn't seem to have any apprehension about the fleeting sunlight nor his current presence here in the wild, as the only of his kind. However, my instincts led me toward the one familiar place where I knew humans, like Ajani, would be. There, he could reconnect with his kind and seek refuge amongst them.

My path through the savannah was laced with the land's whispered lore, the soil's enduring force, and the ancient trails' unveiled guidance. I bore the legacy of the past as a mark of distinction, my mother's memory as a beacon, and realized that my leadership transcended mere navigation through the grasses. It was about preserving a fragile equilibrium between embracing and releasing. Gazing into the expansive horizon, with my mother's wisdom resonating within, I grasped that my role stretched far beyond what I had envisioned. It wasn't about the fury I could unleash on those who had trespassed against us, but about the sanctuary I could provide, the insight I could share, and the future I could forge for our herd.

As twilight draped its calming veil over the savannah, I led the herd along the worn paths known only to those who walk on padded feet and silent hooves. Ajani's presence among us, a solitary figure of quiet contemplation, stirred within me a sense of responsibility. There is safety in numbers for humans as there is for us, and I felt an ancient duty to guide him to the safety of his own kind.

As we approached the village, the sky painted itself with the hues of dusk, the time when light and darkness blend in a fleeting embrace. I sensed Ajani's apprehension, his human fears of the unknown night in the wild lands. But within me, a resolve had taken root, a determination to show him a different facet of the world he thought he knew.

The village lay ahead, a cluster of huts and the flicker of fires, the scent of life and community in the air. I could see the curiosity brighten in Ajani's eyes, a spark of the innate human yearning for exploration. Yet it was the familiar face of the elder of the village who caught my attention, his slender silhouette an echo of kindness in a world often unkind. He was surrounded by children laughing and playing at the village's entrance. As we approached the path leading to the village entrance, we were greeted with smiling faces and, in the distance, another familiar face that emerged and proceeded toward us. It was the leader of Ajani's group.

Efe's face lit up with a mix of astonishment and relief as he spotted Ajani. "Ajani!" he exclaimed, stepping forward with open arms. "You had us worried, wandering off like that!"

Turning towards me, his expression softened into one of deep gratitude. He bowed slightly, his voice sincere as he said, "And you, magnificent one, thank you for watching over him.

We owe you a great debt."

The rest of my herd, sensing the welcoming demeanor of the humans, began to roam leisurely around the village's outskirts, delighting in the generous bounty of apples offered by the trees that dotted the perimeter. The villagers showed no fear and with a welcoming spirit, cleared a path, an open invitation into their midst that spoke of a rare harmony between our kinds.

As I made my way into the village square, for the first time ever, the ground beneath my feet felt familiar yet foreign. I felt the pulse of the village beating in time with my own. And there, in the center of it all, with a presence as commanding as the tallest baobab, was an apple tree that was grander than any I had ever encountered before. Her leaves whispered in the softening light, a sound like water over stones, both ancient and soothing.

With the grace bestowed upon my kind, I approached her, my trunk extending to brush against the rugged bark that told stories of resilience and time. It was a communion, a sharing of life forces, as ancient as the land itself. With the touch, a transfer of energy and of histories intermingled, revealed a realization that she was not only a giver of fruits but also a keeper of secrets and a guardian of the village's soul.

She, who had provided nourishment to my herd via her offspring surrounding the village, now stood before me, a living chronicle of all that was, all that is, and all that will be. I could sense, in each of my feet, that her strength was not in her stature but in her roots, which ran deep and unseen, much like the unspoken bond that connected me to my herd, to the village, to the very essence of life. Her leaves rustled a soft melody, carrying the message that true strength lies in the quiet, unseen places, in the depth of our connections, and in the courage to stand tall through the seasons of life.

As the children continued to play, their laughter weaving

through the air, I absorbed the silent lessons that this tree of life offered. "To grow is not just to reach skyward but to delve into the earth, into the dark and the damp, and to find sustenance in the embrace of the soil. To live is to stand in your place, to flourish where you are planted, and to give back, freely and without reservation."

The village elder's eyes, glazed with the soft sheen of remembrance, met mine as he began to recount a tale from the yesteryears. "Many seasons ago, when I was not much older than your newfound travel companion here, your mother found her way to us," he said, his voice tinged with the warmth of the memory. "She was young, alone, and weary, her eyes wide with the fear of the unknown."

He paused, his gaze drifting to Ola, who stood as a silent witness to this shared history. "Back then, Ola was but a sapling herself, stretching her young branches towards the sky, adorned with her very first blossoms of fruit."

The elder crouched down, scooping a handful of the earth, letting it sift through his fingers, as a gesture that bridged the gap between past and present. "Your mother stumbled into our village, young and alone, pursued by the greed of poachers. It was here, under Ola's young branches, then heavy with her first fruits, that I shared an apple with her."

"It was a moment of trust amidst a world of fear, and in that act, a bond was formed," the elder continued, his eyes reflecting the flicker of flames and the depth of the tale.

"Even in her fear, there was a dignity about her, a regal bearing that your kind carry so naturally. I approached her with caution, with the respect she deserved, speaking in the soft tones we use to soothe restless spirits. In my hand was an apple, the first fruit Ola ever gave," the elder continued, his eyes returning to the present, to me.

"Your mother watched me, her great ears fanning the air,

deciphering my intentions. It was a moment suspended in time. When she finally accepted the apple, it was more than a delicious snack, it was a truce, a silent pact between her world and ours." The elder's voice broke with the weight of the memory.

"We offered her sanctuary, and in time, she offered us trust. A trust that has been passed down to you, her noble daughter." The elder stood, his stature commanding yet gentle.

"Now, as Ola stands witness to the cycles of life, you too have come to us. It's the way of the world, the unending dance of give and take. And just like your mother before you, you've found your way through the wilderness, not just to survive, but to thrive and lead."

His words settled over me like the gentle touch of the setting sun, warming and illuminating. It was a legacy of trust, born from the courage to connect across the divide of species, to find the common ground that life itself offers. And in his story, in the bond formed with my mother, I found a deeper connection to this village, to Ola, and to the very land that cradled us all.

In the elder's words, I found a reflection of my journey—a journey marked by loss but also by the finding of new paths, new understandings, and new connections. The village, with its blend of human and natural rhythms, became a mirror for my own world, reflecting at me the possibilities that unfold when we choose to trust, to share, and to be guardians of one another. And so, beneath Ola's watchful gaze, in the heart of the village, the whispers of trust grew into a dialogue of shared existence, and the lessons of the savannah found a harmonious echo in the lives of those who walked on two legs.

Ajani listened, captivated by the elder's reflection of the past and protected coexistence in a place where the lines between wild and tame blurred into harmony. As I stood there, sharing this space with Ajani and the elder, I understood that my mother's legacy was not just one of loss but also one of kinship with those rare humans who could look into the eyes of an elephant and see a friend and kindred spirit. It was this legacy that I carried forward, not in the shadows of grief but in the light of understanding.

Ajani's gaze met mine, and in his eyes, I saw the dawning of comprehension, the acknowledgment of the silent wisdom that passed between us, the unspoken yet powerful dialogue of respect and recognition.

This night, under the watchful eye of Ola, the silent matriarch, we three stood at the intersection of past and future—human, elephant, and apple tree. Each of us are from a different strand of life's web yet connected by the shared threads of our experiences. This was the essence of trust, spoken not in words but in the shared language of the heart, in the mutual respect for life in all its forms.

7 SILENT EXCHANGES

In the dance of life, where every step is a note in the song of existence, my story is a testament to the power of silent communication, to the bonds that form in the spaces between words. It is a journey of cautious hope, of learning to see beyond the scars of the past, and of finding, in the whisper of trust, a melody that speaks of peace, understanding, and the possibility of coexistence in a world shared by all.

As twilight's curtain fell, Ajani and the village elder exchanged tales and teachings by the flicker of the communal fire. Their voices, rich with stories and sagacity, were like the gentle hum of the savannah's night song, each word a thread in the vibrant fabric of shared history.

My presence was silent, a quiet guardian to their spoken wisdom, yet within me a different kind of dialogue unfolded. Ola, the mother tree at the heart of the village, shared her silent whispers with me, her spirit resonating with mine in a communion deeper than words. Through the rustling of her leaves and the steady pull of life from deep within the earth, she conveyed truths that only the soul could comprehend.

"Zuri," the soft murmur of Ola's voice seemed to say, *"the roots of wisdom run deep, hidden from view but vital. Just as my roots*

anchor me, your experiences have anchored you, lending strength to stand tall." My ears perked, attuned to the unspoken frequency of her spirit, and my heart responded with a gentle rumble, *"I have witnessed loss, and from that, learned the depth of empathy. My journey has been one of sorrow and love, teaching me the resilience of life."*

As the elder spoke of time's passage and the way it carves its mark upon the land and its creatures, Ajani listened, his eyes reflecting the fire's dance, absorbing the layers of meaning in the elder's words. There was a lesson in their exchange that echoed Ola's silent teachings: that life was a cycle of seasons, each one bearing its fruits and its fallow periods, each one a chance to grow, to rest, and renew.

"Life is not just growth," Ola's voice seemed to continue, *"but also the shedding of old leaves, making way for the new. Your hardships have shed like my autumn leaves, Zuri, but they prepare you for a fresh growth, a revival of spirit."*

Within me, an understanding blossomed like the first bud of spring. My trunk reached out, tracing the patterns on Ola's bark, feeling the history etched into her skin. "Your scars are stories," I acknowledged silently, "just as my own are maps of my past, guiding my present."

As the night deepened, Ajani and the elder's conversation drifted towards the notion of purpose. The elder, with a knowing look, gestured towards me, and though no words were exchanged, the meaning was clear: I was a living embodiment of purpose, my very existence a testament to the endurance and connectivity of all life.

Ola's presence offered me a silent counsel, a gentle reminder that even in stillness there is purpose, that even in silence there is communication. *"You, Zuri, are the bridge between past and future, carrying within you the wisdom of lost generations and the hope of those yet to walk the savannah."*

In the sacred silence beneath Ola, I communed with the

great tree, understanding that our lives were intertwined, that her existence nourished not just the body but also the soul. Her lessons were manifold: the quiet grace of being, the dignity of resilience, and the profound wisdom that comes with simply existing in harmony with the world.

The spiritual dialogue between us was a powerful exchange, a sharing of life's essence that transcended the need for speech. To any onlooker, it was just an elephant resting beneath an apple tree, but it was actually a convergence of kindred spirits, each imparting strength to the other.

As the night waned, the lessons gleaned from Ola's silent words, settled within me. I realized that every creature, every plant, every being had a role to play in the great dance of life. Each of us, in our way, contributes to the cycle of life, death, and rebirth. With every sunrise, we are given the chance to embrace our place in the world, to live with intention, and to listen to the wisdom that whispers on the wind and rustles through the leaves.

And so, as the first light of dawn crept over the horizon, my heart swelled with a newfound peace. Beneath Ola's watchful care, surrounded by the echoes of ancestral wisdom, I knew that my path was clear. I would lead my herd not just with the might of my tusks but with the depth of understanding that comes from embracing one's divine nature and discovering the true purpose woven into the very fabric of our being.

It was the power of silence that spoke the loudest truths, teaching us that in the quiet depths of our being lies the knowledge of who we are, the strength of our connections, and the path to coexistence. Through the dance of life's complexities, it was the silent whisper of trust that continued to guide us forward, ever present, and powerful.

8 THE BEAUTIFUL

Beneath the tender branches of Ola, where time seemed to stand still, a profound change had taken root within me. It was not a change visible to the eye, but one that altered the very current of my being. The spiritual dialogue with Ola had instilled a wisdom within me as ancient as the stars strewn across the night sky, and in the silent communion with the village elder and Ajani, I found my purpose crystallizing, sharp and clear like the first light of dawn.

With the dawning of each new day, I felt my spirit lifted by the lessons learned from my silent mentor. Ola had taught me that to lead was not merely to walk ahead but to nurture the roots of those who follow, ensuring they are grounded in strength and wisdom. Like the tree that stands steadfast through the seasons, offering its fruits without expectation, I learned the importance of giving – of offering the fruits of knowledge and the shelter of understanding to the herd I led.

From Ajani, I gleaned the courage to embrace change, to step beyond the borders of the familiar, and to walk into the unknown with a heart open to learning. He was the embodiment of curiosity and the search for a deeper truth, a living example that sometimes the journey we take on the outside reflects the journey within.

The village elder, with his tales spun from the threads of a well-lived life, taught me the value of shared experiences and the power of our choices. He was the weaver at the loom of history, connecting past and present with the wisdom of ages. In his words, I found the metaphor of life: like a river that nourishes the land it traverses, we too must let our experiences flow into the lives of others, enriching and shaping the world around us.

My herd and I moved through the savannah with a newfound purpose, our steps a dance to the music of existence, our hearts beating to the drum of the earth's eternal song. I led them with a serene authority, my actions a testament to the enduring power of trust and the silent strength that had been my inheritance.

Ajani, who had temporarily become a part of our landscape, observed and learned, his human ways slowly harmonizing with the rhythm of the savannah. In the time he spent within the village, his essence had become interwoven with the fabric of our lives. We had become a part of his story, just as he had become a part of ours.

As his time amongst us neared its end, and the moment arrived for him to return to his world, an emotional farewell awaited. With the same solemn grace with which I had first approached Ola, I now stood beneath her grand canopy, reaching for the last apple that clung to her branches. It was a fruit heavy with the sweetness of life's wisdom, a symbol of the knowledge that had been shared, and the bonds that had been formed.

With the gentlest touch, I plucked the apple and offered it to Ajani. It was more than a parting gift; it was a promise, a reminder of the lessons learned and the friendships forged. "Carry this with you," my heart whispered, though no sound escaped my lips. "Let it be a symbol of the journey you have taken, a reminder of the connections that transcend boundaries, and a token of the trust that was restored. Let it also inspire you to always ask 'Why?' as you continue to explore the depths of your own spirit and the world around you."

Ajani accepted the apple with a reverence that spoke of his transformation, his hands cradling it as if it were the most precious treasure. Amid this simple act of giving, I saw the cycle of life turn full circle. The student was now carrying the teacher's wisdom, ready to plant the seeds of his newfound understanding in the soil of another world. This moment encapsulated the essence of our shared experiences, urging us all to question deeper, to understand better, and to never cease asking the questions that challenge us to break the boundaries of our understanding and embrace the limitless possibilities of knowledge and connection.

As he departed, the silhouette of his form against the horizon was not one of a stranger leaving but of a friend embarking on the next leg of his great journey. I stood tall and proud, knowing that the wisdom of Ola, the courage of Ajani, and the lessons of the village elder would continue to live on, as enduring as the ancient land that bore us all. Through this journey, the significance of questioning, of delving into the why, has been etched into our lives, guiding us towards a future ripe with understanding and rich in connection.

As Ajani's silhouette faded and I stood next to Ola, her leaves whispered, *"We are all born with a blank slate. Our experiences and the choices we make because of them, serve as the threads of our existence."*

"That's the answer to my question!" Things are the way that they are because of experiences and choices. Those poachers weren't always filled with hate and greed, but something or a combination of things planted those seeds within them. They made the choice to water them and allow them to grow.

Ajani and the elder have faced their own spectrum of

experiences, choosing to nurture the seeds of love over those of hate. "I too, have the freedom of choice," I reassured myself, a newfound resolve stirring within me. This journey had not only been about survival but about understanding that we all begin with a blank slate, and it is our experiences and the choices we make that ultimately shape who we become and how we view the world and all of the beings within it.

PART III: OLA

Ola
Origin: West African, Yoruba
Meaning: Wealth; Precious

9 WHO IS OLA?

Ola's story is rooted deep within the fertile heart of the village square, yet it began elsewhere, under the wide expanse of the savannah sky, where the cycle of life spun a tale of serendipitous beginnings. There, under the shade of a distant tree, an apple's journey started as a journey that would intertwine with the lives of the gentle giants that roamed the plains.

It was a safari guide, traversing the elephants' ancient pathways, who first extended the hand of gratitude towards the matriarchs of the land. In a gesture that was both an offering of peace and a token of his deep respect, he would give the elephants apples. This was not a mere transaction but a sign of reverence for the silent understanding that existed between man and beast as well as recognition of the elephants' grace in allowing him and his group of tourists to pass through their ancestral grounds.

The elephants, with their deep intelligence and complex emotions, accepted the gift, partaking in the sweetness of the fruit, a symbol of the harmonious relationship that can exist between humanity and the wild. Unbeknownst to the guide, his simple act of appreciation set forth a chain of events that would lead to the birth of Ola.

The apples, sweet and crisp, were consumed under the vastness of the African sky, with the seeds, a representation of potential life, being sown inadvertently as the elephant herd moved across the savannah. It was after a rejuvenating summer downpour that a young man, now an esteemed village elder, discovered what had now grown into a young apple tree. He was as surprised as he was ecstatic, discovering this rarity in the region.

With hope and a vision for the future, the young man made a conscious decision in that moment. He began to build his village around this rare sight, which ultimately became the village square. Whispering a prayer for growth that would interlink the fate of the tree with the pulse of the community, this was the beginning of a legacy that would extend far beyond the shade of a single tree spreading into the lives of all those who would come to know the village square as a place of community, rejuvenation, and celebration.

As Ola grew, so too did her story as it intertwined with that of the villagers. She emerged from the earth, a testament to the enduring spirit of the village and silent monument to the innate strength that comes from simply being. With each year, she stretched further toward the heavens, her limbs caressing the sun's light and moon's glow. She withstood the wrath of storms, her limbs dancing to the tune of resilience, her foliage murmuring tales of perseverance.

As Ola matured, her trunk thickened, her canopy flourished, and she innately continued to bear the fruits of the young elder's foresight. Her apples were a bountiful harvest of ruby and gold, sweet orbs of nourishment that fed both the villagers and the creatures that wandered in from the wilds. Children played in her shade, their laughter as much a part of her music as the rustling of her leaves. The elders sat at her base, sharing stories and wisdom as timeless as the soil.

The villagers, drawn by an inexplicable magnetism, would

often find solace resting against her sturdy trunk, their weary bodies seeking healing after long days of laboring and venturing throughout the vast savannah. In these moments, a profound transference of energy occurred. They spoke of feeling rooted, of a current that flowed from the very core of the earth, through Ola's roots, up her mighty trunk, and into their beings, serving as a rejuvenating exchange that filled them with a renewed sense of vigor and vitality. The process was one of silent communion, where the weary soul could find replenishment in the touch of bark to skin, the shared breath between leaf and lung.

Ola stood as a testament to the healing power of nature, to the profound connection between all living things, and to the ability of the earth to restore and revitalize those who sought its embrace. This energy transference, subtle yet potent, became a cornerstone of the villagers' daily lives. They understood that Ola provided not only sustenance through her fruits but life force through her very existence. In her presence, one could not only taste the sweetness of nature's bounty but also feel the pulsating energy of a life lived in harmonious balance with the world.

Thus, Ola was cherished not just as a provider but as a healer, a giver of life in more ways than one, a silent matriarch whose teachings of patience, resilience, and growth echoed in the hearts of those who knew how to listen. She was the village's unwavering constant, her simple life an elegy to the intricate beauty of existence and a life that whispered to all who would hear that in the dance of give and take, there is a rhythm that sustains, nurtures, and endures.

As the village thrived, the ceaseless progression of seasons etched deep marks upon the life of Ola, the revered apple tree that had stood as a guardian of the village square for countless cycles of the sun and moon. Time, the eternal sculptor, worked its artistry upon her, and the once-laden branches that brimmed with the heavy clusters of fruit began to bear a lighter load.

The villagers understood that in the grand design of nature, there was no room for permanence, that each leaf that yellowed and fell to the ground was a note in the grand symphony of life. It was a demonstration of the beauty and necessity of letting go, of shedding the old to make way for the new. When her leaves regrew, fuller and more vibrant with each passing year, it served as a reminder that there is strength in vulnerability, that renewal follows loss, and that even in dormancy, there is the potential for new growth.

The elder, now stooped with age, watched as the seeds from Ola's apples were planted around the village. It was a cycle of renewal he knew well. It was the old making way for the new, the wisdom of the past nurturing the potential of the future. These saplings, born of Ola's legacy, were the continuation of the community's connection to the earth, a living heritage growing alongside the new generations.

The relationship between Ola and the villagers was symbiotic. She gave without expectation, and they received with gratitude. To the villagers, she was more than a tree. She was a member of their community, a silent elder who taught them the value of patience, the virtue of divine purpose, and the beauty of growth and change.

With each new sapling that broke through the soil's crust, the elder saw the developing of life's continuum, a vivid tapestry woven with threads of the past, present, and future. The wisdom that Ola had absorbed from the sun's warmth, the rain's caress, and the wind's tales, now lived on in these young trees.

They stood as emerging providers, poised to continue the legacy of their originator, each leaf a testament to the tree that had given them life. In the saplings' youthful emergence, was the promise of continuation, of life's unbroken vow to endure through change. The villagers nurtured these offspring with the same dedication that they had given Ola, knowing that as she entered the twilight of her years, the essence of what she had provided would live on. They were the bearers of her heritage, the next chapter in the story that Ola had begun all those years ago.

The conflict within Ola's tale was not one of despair, but of natural transition. The villagers understood that the ebbing of Ola's fruitfulness was not an end but a transformation, a changing of the guard from the old to the new, from the familiar abundance of Ola's harvest to the fresh promise of the saplings' growth. In this acceptance lay the wisdom of the village, a community that saw life not as a collection of static moments, but as an ever-flowing river, where the waters of today carry the reflections of yesterday and the shapes of tomorrow.

Thus, Ola's story was one of gentle conflict, the bittersweet concurrence of aging and renewal, where every diminished apple crop was a nod to the passage of time, and every new sapling was a burst of life's unrelenting spirit. In her decline was the village's rise, in her silence was their song, and in her dusk was the dawn of the new guardians of the village green.

10 WHY AM I STILL HERE?

Rooted deeply in the heart of the village, where whispers of ancient tales mingle with the rustle of the present, I stand as an elder among my offspring. My branches, a testament to countless seasons passed, sway gently in the breeze. As the years have unfolded, the abundance of fruit I once proudly bore has slowly diminished, echoing the inevitable rhythm of time and life's cycles. Yet, within this shift, a question has taken root in my consciousness: "Why am I still here, if I can no longer bear the fruit I once provided in abundance?" This query lingers in the morning air, a silent echo amidst the chorus of dawn.

I found myself in this village not by human design but by a serendipitous gust of fate. Carried as a mere seed to a land where beings like me are rarities, I sprouted in an unlikely sanctuary. However, instead of succumbing to the doubts cast by the unfamiliar, I embraced my existence here with unwavering conviction. Flourishing not in spite of but because of my unique circumstances, I delved deep into the soil, drawing nourishment from hidden sources, while my leaves reached for the caressing sun above, drawing in life's energy, ensuring my survival and eventual thriving in this less than ideal environment.

The journey of an apple tree like me is often symbolic in

human culture, representing knowledge, beauty, and the interconnectedness of life. In reality, apple trees typically thrive for several decades, with our fruit-bearing peak occurring in mid-age. As we age, our productivity will decline, but then what? How do we continue to contribute profoundly to our ecosystem?

As my yields diminish, I find myself reflecting on the value I offer beyond the fruit. Rooted conversations with the younger trees around the village, which sprouted from the seeds of my past seasons' bounty, offer me a broader perspective. They rustle with the vigor of youth, their branches eagerly stretching towards the sky.

"You have given us life," they whisper through the dance of leaves, "a chance to grow, to bear our own fruit, to contribute to the cycle."

It is in this silent dialogue with my offspring that I come to understand the expansive strokes of my existence, painted across the landscape of this village.

As I stood watch in the center of the village, my branches gently swaying in the calm breeze, a familiar yet distant vibration approached. It was the matriarch, of the herd that enjoys the succulent fruit gifted by my offspring, whose presence always carried the echoes of a deep-rooted past. With her, was a face foreign to our village. It was that of a man whose spirit seemed to be searching for deeper truths beyond the visible horizon. The vibrations of their approach stirred memories within me, resonating through the very core of my being.

The vibrations of the present mingled with those of the past as these two beings entered the village for the first time. The elephant's heavy, measured strides upon the earth brought a sense of solemnity and grace, while the man's lighter, tentative footsteps spoke of curiosity and awe. The air around them seemed charged with an unspoken understanding, as if the very atmosphere was aware of the reunion of past and present.

As they both drew nearer, the connection deepened. The energy radiating from the elephant was one of strength and wisdom, honed by her own experiences as a leader, which were familiar qualities that I witnessed within one of her kind, years ago. The foreign man, on the other hand, emitted a vibration of eagerness and openness, a soul ready to embrace new lessons and forge new paths.

I sensed a profound connection with this mythical elephant, a lineage traced back through the mists of time to a moment of shared destiny. Beneath my branches, the village elder greeted them, his face reflecting the wisdom of years and the tranquility of one who understands the cyclical nature of life.

As the village elder began to reflect on some of the family history, of this gentle giant, referred to as Zuri, I learned that it was Zuri's mother who, years ago, had unwittingly played a pivotal role in my very existence.

As a young elephant, Zuri's mother feasted on an apple growing from my mother's vibrant branches. As the seeds, from that precious fruit, we traveled internally throughout that massive being, when she inadvertently released us into the fertile soil of the savannah, eventually leading to my very unique beginning. This connection, woven through the cycles of life, linked us in a tapestry of interdependence and shared history.

This moment was laden with significance, not only for them but for me as well. As the elder continued his recollection, I too recalled another time, one of both serenity and sudden disruption, when Zuri's mother had fled to our village, seeking refuge from the relentless pursuit of poachers. It was here, under my young and blossoming branches, bearing their first fruits, that the village elder, then a young man filled with hope and compassion, offered her the very first piece of fruit that I ever gifted to the world. That act of kindness served as a simple sharing of sustenance and forged a bond of sanctuary and trust that now seemingly lived on through Zuri.

The elder and I share a bond that transcends the mere passage of time. It's a connection forged from years of silent communion, an understanding that speaks to the very essence of existence. He listens to the language of my leaves, the stories told by each blooming flower, and the wisdom held in the cycles of growth and decay.

From me, he has learned the lessons of life's seasons: the importance of deep roots, the power of simplicity, and the beauty of giving without expectation. Even as my form becomes more gnarled and my fruits less frequent, I continue to offer what I can, embodying the truth that purpose and value do not diminish with age.

As I listened to the village elder shift from the story of Zuri's lineage to learning more about and sharing his wisdom with Ajani beneath my canopy, I absorbed their exchange as moonlight through my leaves. The elder spoke of life's purpose, not as a constant, but as something that evolves with each passing season.

"The worth of a being," he explained as he ran his fingers across my aged bark, "lies not only in what they can produce but in the depth of their roots and the shelter they provide." His words resonated within me, a reflection of my own journey through the seasons of growth and change.

From this dialogue, a new understanding began to unfold within me, like the slow opening of a bud into blossom. As Ajani sat against my trunk, his back resting against my bark, I felt a transfer of energy. It was a moment of connection, a sharing of the peace and stillness I offer. This exchange, while silent, was as profound as any spoken word. It reminded me that my role goes beyond fruit-bearing. I am a keeper of calm and a sanctuary for those who seek replenishment and reflection. In this, I found a renewed sense of purpose, realizing that even as my physical contributions might wane, my spiritual offerings flourish.

Amidst this realization, I also reflected on the energy exchange with Zuri, whose presence around the village had become a testament to the interconnectedness of all life. Our non-verbal communication was a silent understanding, passed between us through the still air, that underscored a shared respect for life's cycles. Zuri, in her wisdom, seemed to recognize the deeper role I played within the ecosystem, not merely as a source of physical nourishment but as a symbol of enduring strength and resilience.

This period of reflection and observation has taught me that every phase of existence has its value. The laughter of children playing in my shade, the healing energy I offer to the weary, and the inspiration I provide to those like Ajani, seeking to understand their path, are all facets of my purpose. Just as the villagers have learned to adapt and find new ways to contribute to their community, I too have discovered that my influence extends beyond the tangible.

The wisdom garnered from these interactions culminates in a profound realization: my purpose is not static but dynamic, evolving with each season. It is a lesson that each being, each entity, whether a person, elephant, or a tree, comes to learn in their own time. In every season of life, there is a unique purpose waiting to be discovered and fulfilled.

As I continue to stand here, rooted in the heart of the village, I serve as a living reminder that life's true value is measured not only in what we can produce, but in the shelter we provide, the connections we foster, and the tranquility we offer to the souls that seek solace beneath our branches.

Thus, as the village elder often says, asking "Why am I still here?" is not a question of doubt, but an invitation to explore deeper truths about our existence. It is a call to recognize the shifts in our purpose and to embrace the myriad of ways we can continue to enrich the lives around us, regardless of the season we find ourselves in. In this understanding, I find peace, knowing that my continued presence in this village is a testament to the enduring impact one can have, simply by being true to their nature and embracing the changes that come with time.

I cherish the moments when villagers rest against my trunk, their bodies releasing the burdens of their days. They seek not the apples I once offered but the sanctuary provided by my enduring presence. In their quiet company, I feel an exchange of energy, which serves as a subtle yet profound reminder of my ongoing role as a nurturer of spirits.

As I continue to stand here, a steadfast elder in this village, I embrace the evolving nature of my purpose. From providing abundant fruit to offering shade and sanctuary, each season of my life offers new ways to support the community around me. Just as the villagers adapt and grow through their experiences, so too do I find new meaning in my continued existence. And in asking "Why am I still here?" I am reminded of the cycle of life, of giving and receiving, and of the endless opportunities to enrich the world, simply by being.

11 THE LAST APPLE

My simplicity, devoid of ostentation, is a reflection of life's core truths. Each day, I fulfill my role, offering shade, beauty, and sustenance, and facilitating moments of community and connection. The elder, whose life parallels the journey of quiet growth and humble service, sees in me a living lesson: to live is to give, to persist is to impart wisdom, and to age is to have embraced the full spectrum of existence.

The villagers, treating me with the reverence one might show a cherished elder, tend to the young saplings sprouted from my seeds, a gesture that ensures the continuation of my legacy and the enrichment of our shared environment. In return, I stand sentinel over them, my branches a chronicle of our intertwined histories.

Beneath my canopy, generations converge as the elder shares tales with the village's youth, their laughter and dreams mingling with the soft rustling of my leaves. This spot, shaded and sacred, is a cradle for the community's heartbeat, where the cycle of life dances on, guided by the timeless pivot that I have become. The new orchard, born from my legacy, blossoms as a testament to the village's dedication to growth, continuity, and the nurturing of future dreams.

As the seasons march on, transforming the savannah with their endless cycle of renewal and letting go, my branches are twisted with the wisdom of age but continue to reach and embrace the stories carried by the wind. The villagers listen, finding in my presence the whispers of history, the joy of their children, and the dignity of their forebears. To them, and to Zuri, who recognizes my silhouette from afar, I am a beacon of resilience, a source of life's sustenance, and a promise of rest and renewal.

In this grand tapestry of existence, I remain steadfast. Though my trunk shows the marks of time, I stand as a testament to life's enduring strength, to the wisdom that comes from simply being. To the elder, I am more than a tree. I am a fellow journeyer, bearing witness to the cycle of life, from the first tender shoot to the fullness of bloom and beyond. To the village's children, who play in my shadow, I am a guardian of their youth, a keeper of their laughter.

And in the quiet of night, when the elder rests against me, gazing up at the stars that tell the stories of his ancestors, we share a connection deep and profound, rooted in the earth and stretching to the heavens. Together, we understand that life, in all its complexity and simplicity, is a dance of giving and receiving, of teaching and learning, of growing and letting go.

In this way, my life continues to unfold as a silent witness to the passage of time, a bearer of shade, beauty, and wisdom. My existence, though marked by fewer fruits, remains rich and meaningful, a testament to the quiet, enduring power of nature's simplest gifts. Through me, the village learns the value of presence over abundance, of the lessons taught through the act of living, and of the beauty in fulfilling one's purpose with grace and dignity.

In this new understanding, I embrace the shifts in my purpose, recognizing that with each stage of growth comes a different way to serve, to add value to the tapestry of life around me. Just as the villagers find new ways to contribute to their community as they journey through life, so too do I find new meaning in my continued existence.

Moreover, my legacy lives on through the trees that have grown from my seeds, each one a testament to the cycles of life, to the importance of giving without expectation. They are my contribution to the future, ensuring that the village remains a place of abundance and beauty long after my last apple has fallen.

Our purpose, it seems, is like the river that flows through the village – ever-changing, adapting to the contours of the land, nourishing life in myriad ways. And so, I stand here, more than just an apple tree – I am a guardian, a guide, and a giver of life, embodying the lesson that in every season, there is a unique purpose waiting to be discovered and fulfilled.

As my narrative unfurls, like the gentle spread of leaves towards the sun, let it serve as a testament to the subtle yet profound influence of existence, echoing the sacred cycle of nurturing and flourishing inherent in nature. In the tapestry of life, where the clamor for material wealth often overshadows the quiet gifts of the spirit, may my tale rekindle an appreciation for the foundational pillars of connection, generosity, and purpose. Within the weave of my years, marked by the seasonal gifts of fruit and the steadfast presence of shade, discover a call to embrace the elemental bonds that unite us, a reminder that our truest contributions stem from what we impart to others, not from our accumulations.

The moment when Zuri tenderly delivered my final apple Into Ajani's hands was laden with the weight of legacy and renewal. This exchange, bridging the worlds of nature and humanity, symbolized not only the transfer of nourishment but also the passing of wisdom—a wisdom that speaks of resilience, of the shared journey of life, and of the profound cycle of giving that underpins existence. As Ajani takes this piece of me back to his own soil, planting the seeds nestled within, he does more than simply sow future trees; he embeds into his realm the essence of my spirit, ensuring that the lessons learned beneath my boughs take root in a new land.

This act of planting carries with it a multitude of significances, each seed a promise of growth, of grounding, and of the continuous flow of life's energies. For Ajani, these seeds represent a tangible connection to the lessons of simplicity, purpose, and generosity he absorbed in the village. As they grow, branching out and up towards the sky, they will serve as a living reminder to remain anchored in his truths, to cultivate his gifts with the intention of sharing, and to live a life that, like mine, nourishes and shelters those around him.

Moreover, the act of nurturing these seeds into saplings, and eventually into fruit-bearing trees, mirrors the journey Ajani has embarked upon—a journey of self-discovery, of peeling away the layers to reveal his core essence, and of understanding that his true wealth lies in the impact he makes, the connections he fosters, and the legacy he leaves behind. Just as I have become more than an apple tree in the eyes of the village, Ajani's journey with the seeds of my last fruit symbolizes his transformation and the spreading of the wisdom he has garnered.

This union of past and present underscored the profound impact of simple acts and the enduring nature of relationships that transcend generations. I am a witness to the enduring bonds formed under my canopy, and a testament to the belief that from small seeds, great things grow. It was a vivid reminder that the seeds we sow, whether literal or metaphorical, grow beyond our immediate sight and can nourish lives far into the future.

Thus, as my story melds into the fabric of Ajani's life and into the hearts of those who wander through these words, let it ignite a spark to seek simplicity, to nurture the connections that bind us to one another and to the earth, and to recognize that each of us carries, within, the potential to sow seeds of change. May the growth of these seeds, from my last fruit carried afar by Ajani, remind us all to stand firm in our purpose, to share abundantly the fruits of our being, and to cherish the cycles of life that connect every breath, every act, and every heart in the grand, beautiful mosaic of existence. My narrative should beckon us to question, to delve deeper, and to always ask, "Why?"—a simple question that invites us to uncover more meaningful truths about our existence and our interactions with the world around us.

12 SYMBOLISM EXPLAINED

Now it is time for us to look deeper into the lives of the beings within this book, not just as characters in a story, but as symbols and echoes of our innermost journeys. As you continue, it will be revealed what some of the various characters and experiences were meant to represent but there are also others that will be left for you to decide. The symbolism woven throughout this book presents a reflection of life's complexities and the universal quest for purpose and understanding. Are you ready to look in the mirror?

Ajani: You and Me

Ajani's narrative is a vivid illustration of the internal struggle many face against the rigid frameworks of societal expectations, cultural norms, and the predefined milestones of success in careers and community life. Every experience, whether pleasant or painful, throughout his life led to the moment in his life where we joined him in his deciding moment to pursue change and purpose.

Ajani's deliberate departure into uncharted territories is a powerful metaphor for the transformative journey of self-discovery and personal growth that many of us embark upon.

This journey frequently necessitates a form of isolation, a deliberate stepping back from the noise and demands of our daily lives to focus intently on our own development. This period of solitude is not about loneliness but about creating space for introspection, learning, and growth.

His tale is a universal echo of the discomfort that arises when we find ourselves confined by the boundaries of our current existence, yearning for a meaning that transcends the mundane. Often times, for us, this requires a period of isolation from our present environment, to include people, places, and things that have contributed to our discomfort. Ajani's flight to an unknown land, served as that isolation.

In real life, this might manifest in various ways that signal a departure from the norm, much like Ajani's. For instance, choosing to spend a Friday night immersed in a personal project or a book rather than joining peers at the club can be a form of isolation that prioritizes personal interests and long-term goals over immediate social gratification. Similarly, the decision to remain single, shunning the distractions and emotional turmoil that can accompany serial dating, allows for a period of self-reflection and understanding, fostering a stronger sense of self before entering a new relationship.

Isolation for the sake of personal growth can also mean dedicating months or even years to learn and master a new skill or trade. Consider the artist who retreats to their studio, turning down social invitations to devote themselves to their craft, or the entrepreneur who spends every waking moment building a business from the ground up. These are modern-day examples of Ajani's journey, where the isolation from familiar environments and routines is a conscious choice to foster personal development and achieve something greater.

Famous figures throughout history have taken similar paths of isolation for personal growth. Bill Gates, for example, is known for his "Think Weeks," during which he isolates himself in a cabin in the woods, away from the distractions of daily life, to read and think deeply about future endeavors. Similarly, J.K. Rowling retreated to the quiet of cafes to write the Harry Potter series, distancing herself from the chaos of her then-circumstances to focus on creating the world of Hogwarts.

Ajani's story, and the stories of real-life individuals who have chosen isolation to focus on their growth, highlight a crucial lesson: sometimes, stepping away from the crowd, from the familiar, and from the routine is necessary to find our true path. It is in these moments of solitude that we can listen more closely to our inner voice, challenge our limits, and emerge stronger, more focused, and ready to tackle the challenges that lie ahead. This form of isolation is not an end but a beginning, a necessary detour on the journey to fulfilling our potential and realizing our dreams.

Ajani's initial isolation consisted of self-reflection and mental recuperation. After his period of mental rehab, he decided to increase the intensity and embark on a guided safari. The safari tour is emblematic of life's unpredictable journey.

While the rest of the tour group follows Efe, Ajani embodies that rare fragment of the population endowed with the audacity to question the status quo and break away from the safety net woven by societal conventions. His deliberate step away from Efe's lead and the marked trail, underlines a profound decision to forge a unique destiny, to explore uncharted land in pursuit of personal truth and fulfillment. This act of defiance against the conventional safari tour is a metaphor for the structured traditions and career paths that many adhere to, highlighting the courage required to sculpt one's trajectory based on individual aspirations rather than societal blueprints.

As we observe Ajani's venture into the unknown, his journey is reminiscent of visionary entrepreneurs such as Steve Jobs and Elon Musk, who transcended traditional pathways to carve niches that would eventually redefine the landscape of their respective industries. Through their stories and Ajani's fictional expedition, we are reminded of the intrinsic value and transformative potential that lies in pursuing one's path. This narrative champion the notion that true growth, innovation, and the essence of personal success are discovered not within the confines of the well-trodden path but in the wilderness of the unknown.

Ajani's saga is more than just a tale of exploration; it is a beacon for those yearning to break free from the proverbial rat race, an encouragement to embrace the uncertainty that comes with charting one's course. His separation from Efe and the safari symbolizes the leap of faith required to transcend the familiar terrains of traditional employment and/or societal expectations that make up the "American Dream," encouraging us to venture into the vastness of our potential. It serves as a testament to the courage it takes to leave the safety of the known, for the potential of the unknown, to trade security for the thrill of self-discovery.

The Safari: The 'American Dream'

Ajani's experience on the safari tour is a vivid illustration of life's journey toward the "American Dream," which is a journey fraught with expectations, societal pressures, and the seductive illusion of a path paved with success and material wealth. The tour, with its winding trails and unpredictable sightings, is a microcosm of life's broader voyage, where each of us is both a passenger and a navigator, seeking out the treasures of existence while often unsure of what lies around the next bend.

The tourists, with their cameras at the ready and their hearts filled with anticipation, are representatives of the working-class individuals of the world. They embark on the journey, hoping to capture a glimpse of the exotic and the extraordinary—to collect memories and experiences that align with society's definition of a life well-lived. They represent the hope and the hustle of those who chase the dream, armed with the belief that the path they are on will lead to the rewards they have been promised.

The safari, much like life, is unpredictable. It promises encounters with the magnificent—the success and luxuries we associate with having 'made it'. Yet, it also harbors the potential for the unexpected. Just as the tourists on the tour find themselves facing the raw and untamed aspects of the wilderness, so too do we confront the realities of life that are often harsh, unscripted, and wholly different from what we envisioned.

In this safari called life, our experiences and encounters are teachers in disguise. Some are gentle in their lessons, offering moments of beauty and joy. Others are stern, forcing us to confront our fears and to question the paths we've chosen. There are those encounters that reaffirm our chosen pursuits, and then there are those that cause us to stray from the beaten path in search of deeper meaning and fulfillment—a pursuit that is not about a dream defined by others but about a purpose that resonates with the core of our being.

Ajani's decision to venture away from the safety of the guided tour is a leap of faith, a step toward self-discovery. It is a decision that many face in their lifetimes: to continue along the well-trodden path or to carve a new trail, one that may lead to the unknown but promises the possibility of personal revelation and authentic existence. It is in this brave deviation from the expected route that one often finds their true calling, not in the echoes of what has been, but in the silence of what is yet to come.

This safari tour is more than just a pursuit of fleeting excitement; it is the embodiment of our own existential expedition. Each of us, in our quest for the "American Dream" or its equivalent, must navigate through the terrain of life with both caution and daring. The tour reminds us that while we may not know all we will encounter on this journey, the true rewards are often found not in the reaching of a destination but in the richness of the voyage itself.

The Safari Guide (Efe): Societal Norms

The tour guide, Efe, with his map and compass in hand, strides confidently at the forefront of the safari expedition, embodying the societal norms and traditional career paths, within the 'American Dream,' which are meant to guide us through life's 'jungle.' Efe, with his wealth of knowledge and navigational expertise, represents the societal structures that, while occasionally providing direction, can also keep us within the confines of convention, prompting the question of whether we are merely following the path laid out for us or our own unique trail.

In the vast expanse of life, where each path can lead to countless destinations, the tour guide offers a scripted narrative that promises success and security. Like our careers, he provides the tools, the knowledge, and the pathway to navigate through the dense undergrowth of societal expectations and professional aspirations. He is the assurance against the fears that lurk in the shadows of our Ambition, the steady hand that guides us through the terrain we would hesitate to traverse alone.

The followers, those excited tourists with cameras slung over their shoulders and eyes wide with anticipation, symbolize the masses. They are the embodiment of societal conformity, the individuals who, by choice or necessity, remain within the guided tour of the conventional workforce. Their journey, marked by the stops designated by the tour guide, mirrors the structured progression of traditional careers—the milestones of success defined by external validation and societal benchmarks.

In this journey, the tour guide's role is both essential and limiting. He is the guardian of the traditional path, providing valuable knowledge and resources, yet his route is but one of many. The jungle of life, vast and untamed, holds secrets and wonders that can only be uncovered through personal venture and risk.

Thus, the tour guide, in leading the way, also unwittingly illuminates the limitations of following. He is a necessary part of the journey, a figure of guidance and support, but his path is not the only destination. In stepping away, Ajani and by extension, the reader, is reminded that true exploration, growth, and understanding often begin where the guided tour ends.

Zuri: The Spiritual Leader

Zuri, with her silent but potent leadership, reflects the spiritual leaders among us. She shows us that wisdom often comes cloaked in the form of adversity. Her tale teaches us that leadership is as much about following as it is about leading, and that true leaders must grow up fast, honing their instincts, and learning from their experiences to guide others effectively. Zuri's struggle with trust after witnessing her mother's death at the hands of poachers highlights the delicate balance leaders must strike between vulnerability and strength.

Like spiritual leaders, such as the Dalai Lama or Desmond Tutu, Zuri learns to lead with poise, even in the face of great personal loss. She comes to understand that rationalization is a powerful tool. Not all humans are inherently harmful, just as not all situations in our lives are black and white. Her leadership style is reminiscent of those who lead by example and guide without coercion, inspiring trust through their actions. Just as Zuri ultimately leads her herd to the village, reflecting her growth and understanding, spiritual leaders guide their followers towards enlightenment and awakening. The village epitomizes consciousness and a place of awakening where one can find solace and community. The community within the village shows us that consciousness is not a solitary pursuit but one that thrives within a supportive network.

In this unfolding narrative, Zuri becomes a beacon of guidance for Ajani, much like the North Star leading sailors through tumultuous seas. Her ability to discern the inherent goodness within Ajani, despite her own reservations about humans, underscores the essence of true leadership. It's not about leading those who are easy to lead but about seeing the potential in everyone. Zuri's role in Ajani's journey is a testament to the transformative power of trust and the willingness to follow. Just as a river carves its path through the landscape, patiently and persistently shaping the earth, Zuri's gentle guidance carves a path for Ajani towards a deeper understanding of himself and the world around him. Sometimes it takes a guide to introduce us to new levels of awareness.

Ajani's readiness to place his trust in Zuri, to follow her lead into the unknown, mirrors the leap of faith required of us when we choose to follow those who inspire us towards growth, like mentors. This act of trust is not a surrender of autonomy but an acknowledgment of the value that others, especially those who have navigated their own adversities, can add to our journey. Just as a child trusts the parents to nurture and raise them into adulthood, Ajani trusts Zuri to lead him to new realms of understanding. Their dynamic is a profound illustration of the interdependent relationship between leader and follower, where vulnerability meets strength, and where the willingness to be led is as crucial as the wisdom to lead.

The Village: Consciousness

Nestled in the embrace of nature, where the whispers of the past blend with the breath of the present, lies the village as a symbol of consciousness in its most profound form. It is here, within its unassuming boundaries, that the essence of awareness, understanding, and communal unity flourishes. The village represents the awakening to consciousness, a state of being where the fog of societal indoctrination lifts to reveal the vibrant hues of true existence.

Zuri, in her journey from the wild to the heart of the village, embodies the spiritual leaders who shepherd us into this realm of heightened awareness. The village, with its simple truths and harmonious living, stands as a testament to what can be achieved when individuals come together, guided by a leader who has ventured through the darkness to find light. It is a microcosm of the wider world, where the potential for collective consciousness exists but often lies dormant, awaiting the right catalyst.

The village's very fabric is woven with the threads of open-heartedness and open-mindedness. Those who enter its domain are invited to shed the layers of preconception, to question the narratives they have been fed, and to embark on a journey of self-discovery. It is a place where the soul is nurtured, where the mind is expanded, and where the heart is opened to the boundless possibilities of understanding and connection.

This awakening is not a solitary endeavor. Like Zuri leading her herd, it requires a willingness to follow and to trust in the guidance of those who have navigated the path of enlightenment and have emerged with the wisdom to lead others. The village flourishes because it is a community of like-minded souls, each contributing to the collective consciousness, each learning from the other, and each finding comfort in the shared pursuit of deeper understanding.

In the real world, just as in the village, the journey to consciousness can radically alter one's perception of existence. Once exposed to the light of awareness, the shadows of ignorance and conformity lose their hold. The world is seen not as a fixed reality but as a fluid tapestry of experiences, each offering lessons and opportunities for growth. The village, in its simplicity and authenticity, represents the ideal of what our communities could be if we embraced consciousness, if we sought to understand rather than to judge, to connect rather than to divide.

The transition into this awakened state is transformative. It challenges the very foundations upon which our lives have been built, urging us to question, to explore, and to redefine what we hold to be true. It is a rebirth of sorts, a shedding of old skins for a new way of being that is in harmony with the deeper truths of existence.

For those who have experienced this awakening, the village becomes more than just a place. It becomes a symbol of homecoming. It is the point of return where the journey makes sense, where the scattered pieces of the puzzle come together to reveal a picture of profound beauty and complexity. The village, with its open doors and open hearts, beckons to all seekers of truth, offering a place of refuge, understanding, and unconditional acceptance.

In this narrative, the village is the nexus where paths converge, where lessons are learned, and where life is lived in its most authentic form. It stands as a beacon of hope, a reminder that beyond the confines of our conditioned existence lies a vast expanse of consciousness waiting to be explored. It invites us to break free from the chains of the mundane, to venture into the realms of the unknown, and to discover the boundless potential that resides within us all.

The Village Elder: The Beacon of Spiritual Wisdom

In the heart of the village, amidst the bustle of daily life and the serene whispers of Ola's leaves, stands a figure of quiet strength and profound wisdom. The village elder, embodying the essence of spiritual teachers, guides through example and experience. His life is a testament to the virtues of simplicity, patience, and an unwavering commitment to the divine path.

The village elder, with his gentle demeanor and eyes that have witnessed the unfolding of countless seasons, represents the spiritual teachers who walk among us. These are the individuals whose existence is dedicated not to the pursuit of material wealth or the accolades of their peers, but to the fulfillment of a higher calling. They don't seek to please the world, but a higher power, which guides their actions and teachings.

Through his interactions with the villagers and the tender care he extends towards Ola and her offspring, the elder teaches without the need for grand declarations. His life is his lesson and serves as a beacon of hope and a source of light for those seeking understanding in a world often shrouded in complexity. He demonstrates that true wisdom does not shout from the rooftops but whispers in the quiet moments, in the acts of kindness that go unnoticed, in the simple yet profound truths that govern existence.

This spiritual teacher does not impose his views but rather offers a perspective broad enough to encompass the vastness of human experience. He encourages exploration, understanding, and the discovery of consciousness within oneself. Through his example, the villagers learn that the path to enlightenment is not about adherence to rigid doctrines but about the openness to question, to seek, and to grow.

Simplicity is the elder's solace, and it becomes a powerful lesson in a world increasingly driven by consumerism and the accumulation of wealth. He shows that true contentment and peace are not found in the abundance of possessions but in the richness of the soul. His life is a reminder that in simplicity, there is clarity, and in clarity, there is the space for genuine spiritual growth.

The elder's relationship with the village, and by extension, his role as a spiritual teacher, is a delicate dance of guidance and letting go. He understands that everyone must walk their path, make their mistakes, and find their truth. His wisdom is not a map but a compass, offering direction but allowing each soul the freedom to explore the terrain of their spiritual journey.

In the documentary of the village's life, the elder stands as a pivotal figure, a custodian of the past and a visionary for the future. His teachings, imbued with the essence of spirituality, ripple through the community, touching lives and transforming hearts. He is the silent guardian of consciousness, nurturing the seeds of awareness and watching as they bloom into the vibrant flowers of enlightenment.

As the closing chapter of our story weaves together the symbolism of each character and their journeys, the village elder's narrative stands as a profound reflection on the role of spiritual teachers in society. They are the lighthouses in the stormy seas of life, guiding us not to the safety of the shore but to the depths of our being, where the true treasure of existence lies hidden. In their simplicity, their wisdom, and their unwavering faith, they remind us that the journey of life, with all its trials and tribulations, is also a journey of incredible beauty, wonder, and the eternal quest for the light within.

Ola: Spirituality

Ola, the stoic apple tree at the village's heart, is a paragon of spirituality. The village, where each character finds refuge, represents the consciousness within us all and the awakening that many experience when exposed to new philosophies, cultures, or spiritual teachings.

Ola's deep roots and expansive branches represent our connection to the earth and each other, as well as the purpose and growth we all seek. Ola imparts her lessons without uttering a word, emphasizing that spirituality is not always a vocal journey but one deeply etched in our actions and presence. Her existence, offering nourishment and shelter, serves as a reminder that our impact on the world often lies in our quiet contributions. Ola's lessons are multifaceted, teaching us about resilience, as she stands tall through the seasons, about generosity, as she provides apples to all, and about growth, as she continually reaches skyward while keeping her roots firmly planted.

Consider figures like Mother Teresa or Thich Nhat Hanh, whose lives were testaments to the power of silent, steadfast spirituality. They showed us that spirituality could be a shared journey, one that binds communities together under a common goal of growth and exploration. Ola's teachings are reflections of their messages: that living in accordance with one's true purpose can offer as much to the world as any grand gesture.

In the narrative of Ola's origin, there lies a tale of serendipity and vision that bound the fate of a young man, destined to become the village elder, to a young and thriving apple tree. When the elder, then a young man, first laid eyes on Ola, she was boasting her very first layer of branches. In a land where the sight of an apple tree was as rare as a desert rose, he perceived her existence as a beacon of hope and symbol that this place was marked for something extraordinary.

This young man, with dreams as broad as the horizon, felt an immediate kinship with Ola. He saw in her more than just a tree; she was a promise of fertility, community, and spiritual abundance. Compelled by a deep sense of purpose, he chose to establish his future around her, envisioning a village that thrived in symbiotic harmony with nature, with Ola and spirituality, at its core.

His decision to embrace and nurture this young tree bearing her first fruit laid the foundation for a community where values of unity, provision, and spiritual connection would deeply root and spread their branches wide, echoing the cycles of life where nurturing and being nurtured go hand in hand, creating a symbiosis that defines the essence of existence.

Within the essence of Ola's being, a profound legacy was nurtured through the fruit she bore, which transcended the singular existence of an apple tree, embodying the spirit of spirituality itself. Each fruit she bore was filled with the essence of her being, and the seeds within those apples carried the potential for spreading her spiritual legacy far beyond her physical location. Villagers carefully gathered these seeds and planted them in nurturing soil, where they sprouted into young saplings reaching skyward, flourishing into strong, generous trees much like Ola herself. This act of planting and nurturing the seeds mirrored the way spirituality spreads, subtly and profoundly, infusing the land and its people with wisdom and vitality. Each new tree that grew from Ola's seeds stood as a living symbol of the cycle of life, embodying the principles of generosity and interconnectedness. Through these trees, Ola's spiritual influence blossomed across the landscape, demonstrating how the core of one's spirit can resonate through generations, significantly enriching lives beyond one's immediate existence.

The moment Zuri gently plucked Ola's last apple from its branch, offering it to Ajani, was laden with symbolism and profound meaning. This gesture was not just a sharing of fruit, but a passing of wisdom and token of the journey Ajani had undertaken. The apple, a product of Ola's resilience and generosity, embodied the lessons of strength, the virtue of silence, and the importance of deeply rooting oneself while reaching out to offer support to others. For Ajani, taking this apple back home was like carrying a piece of the village's soul as a reminder of the unity and peace he had found in this place, and the silent wisdom that had guided him towards a deeper understanding of his own purpose.

This act underscored the importance of taking the lessons we learn and the growth we experience and sharing them with others. Just as Ola's fruit gave life to new trees, the knowledge and insight Ajani gained from his journey are meant to be sown into the lives of those he encounters, spreading the seeds of consciousness far beyond his immediate surroundings.

It is a message to the reader that each of us carries within us the potential to influence change, to nourish the growth of others, and to contribute to the collective awakening of humanity. In sharing the fruit of our experiences, we perpetuate a cycle of learning, giving, and growing that transcends time and space, nurturing the roots of a global village connected by the shared pursuit of understanding, compassion, and purpose.

13 THE HARMONY OF EXISTENCE

In the grand symphony of life, each character and each symbol, plays a critical note. Together, they create a melody that speaks to the heart of human existence—a harmony of seeking, growth, connection, and enlightenment. This book, in its exploration of these themes, invites readers to embark on their journeys of self-discovery, to question the status quo, and to seek out the deeper meanings that lie just beneath the surface of daily life.

The stories of Ajani, Zuri, and Ola are but reflections of our own, mirrors into which we are invited to gaze deeply. In their struggles, their triumphs, and their moments of insight, we find echoes of our own experiences and reminders of the shared journey of all humanity.

As we turn the final page, we are left with an invitation to explore the enormity of our inner landscapes, to embrace the challenges and uncertainties of our paths, and to seek out the connections that bind us to each other and to the earth. It is a call to live not just in the world but with the world, in a state of conscious awareness that elevates every moment, every interaction, and every decision into a step along the path to our highest selves.

This narrative is a rope that binds us not just to the characters within its pages but to each other and to the timeless quest for understanding, purpose, and peace. It reminds us that, in the dance of life, we are all both leaders and followers, teachers and students, seekers and finders. In the harmony of existence, every note is essential, every voice matters, and every story contributes to the unfolding of the grandest tale of all— the story of who we are, who we are becoming, and WHY we are   here.

CALL TO ACTION

In crafting this narrative, I have sought to intertwine a group of lessons, each aligned with the experiences of Ajani, Zuri, Ola, and others, serving as symbols of the deeper journeys we all undertake. This book is more than a collection of stories; it's an invitation to reflect and to ask ourselves the potent question that underscores our existence: "Why don't we ask why?"

The act of asking "why" sets apart those who navigate life with a proactive curiosity from those who might prefer the comfort of unchallenged routines. It is the difference between accepting the world as it is presented and daring to question the underlying currents that shape our reality. People who regularly engage with this question often find themselves on a path of accelerated growth and expanded understanding. They are the ones who unravel the complexities of societal norms, who challenge outdated traditions, and who innovate by seeing beyond the visible.

However, not everyone is comfortable with this question. Some shy away, not out of fear of the unknown alone but also because of the discomfort that the answers might bring. For instance, in the realm of parenting, we often hear a child's curious inquiries met with "because I said so" or "that's just how it is." This response shuts down further questioning and instills a pattern of accepting without understanding, mirroring larger societal tendencies where questioning is discouraged. If you don't know or understand 'why,' are you qualified to lead those who are curious and asking? As you read through these final pages, you will come across 4 different calls to action that I challenge each of you to act upon.

Lifestyles:

In socio-economic discussions, asking why the rich get richer while the poor get poorer, can reveal uncomfortable truths about systemic inequalities and personal responsibilities that some find too challenging or indicting to engage with.

In the journey of life, we often find ourselves drawn to the allure of luxury items, attention, and a lifestyle that seems to promise happiness and fulfillment. It is crucial, however, to understand why we yearn for these things. Are they truly a reflection of our deepest desires, or are they merely symbols of success imposed by societal standards?

I challenge you, to expedite your pursuit of these material desires. Acquire the luxury car, the designer clothes, the sprawling mansion, and immerse yourself in the lifestyle you believe will bring you joy. It is through this process that you will quickly discover the temporary nature of such happiness. Often, we find that once we achieve these goals, the satisfaction they bring is fleeting. This realization is vital, as it can lead to a deeper understanding of what genuinely enriches our lives. It compels us to seek fulfillment in more enduring pursuits like relationships, personal growth, and contributions to our communities. Let this be your first call to action: to explore and understand the true sources of long-term happiness and fulfillment, beyond the immediate gratification that material possessions offer.

Relationships:

In relationships, unresolved traumas often linger because delving into the "why" can open painful wounds that many prefer to leave untouched, fearing that such explorations might lead to more discomfort or require changes they feel unprepared to make.

Relationships often serve as mirrors, reflecting not just our joys but also the traumas and unresolved issues we carry. The reluctance to explore the deeper "why" behind our actions or feelings in relationships stems from the fear and discomfort tied to uncovering painful truths. For example, someone may avoid discussing past infidelities or childhood neglect with their partner, fearing that acknowledging these issues could disrupt the precarious balance of their current happiness. This avoidance can lead to a cycle of superficial interactions that fail to address underlying issues, potentially stifling growth in both individuals.

However, confronting these difficult questions is crucial for healing and developing stronger, more authentic connections. Consider a couple where one partner has experienced abandonment. If this issue remains unaddressed, it may manifest as clinginess or distance in the relationship, creating tension and misunderstanding. By courageously confronting and discussing their fears, the couple can work towards understanding and reassurance, potentially transforming their relationship into a source of strength and security.

I urge you, to embrace the courage to ask "why" in your relationships. Investigate the roots of your fears, desires, and reactions. This process, while challenging, is often the first step toward healing and deepening your connections with others. Let this be your second call to action: to pursue authenticity and depth in your relationships, and to use the insights gained to foster greater understanding and intimacy.

Beliefs:

In the realm of beliefs, particularly within religious contexts, there's often a hesitation to question the origins or validity of our faith. This reluctance can stem from a deep-seated reverence for tradition and a fear of what might be discovered if we start to question the doctrines we've been taught. For instance, many people accept religious teachings purely on faith, without considering historical contexts, translations, or interpretations that may alter their understanding. This uncritical acceptance is often rooted not just in reverence but also in a fear of the existential crises that such inquiries might provoke.

This phenomenon is not limited to religion; it can be seen in other belief systems and ideologies where questioning is discouraged, and unchallenged compliance is praised. For example, in some political or cultural groups, questioning the status quo can be seen as disloyal or disruptive, discouraging individuals from expressing their doubts or seeking deeper truths.

The skepticism surrounding vaccines and their overall intentions, showcased a divide across the globe. One group sought to understand the science and implications, asking "why" at every step, while others preferred not to delve too deeply, perhaps fearing what they might uncover or mistrusting the responses they might find. Both sides, regardless of who fared better, experienced losses. Relationships were destroyed, families were torn apart, and many jobs and opportunities were snatched away. Now, looking in hindsight, take a second and think about why that was.

I encourage you, to embrace a spirit of inquiry in all areas of belief. Dare to ask "why" about the doctrines you follow and the teachings you accept. Explore their origins, understand different interpretations, and consider their relevance in today's world. This pursuit of knowledge will not only deepen your understanding but also empower you to make more informed choices about the beliefs you choose to embrace. Let this be

115

your third call to action: to question, to learn, and to grow in your understanding of the beliefs that shape your world.

Career Growth:

Many of you, currently reading this have experienced reaching a career peak only to find that advancing further requires different skills, such as enhanced emotional intelligence, a shift from technical expertise to strategic thinking, or even a complete change in career direction. Similarly, personal relationships may evolve where qualities like openness, vulnerability, and empathy become necessary to deepen connections that were once maintained through surface-level interactions.

"What got you here, won't get you there." This maxim underscores the necessity of adaptation and growth beyond our current strategies and behaviors. As we evolve, the methods and mindsets that previously led to success may no longer suffice for new challenges or opportunities.

This lesson is vital for anyone undergoing transitions, whether in careers, personal lives, or spiritual paths. It encourages us to continually reassess our tools and approaches, ensuring they are aligned with our evolving goals and environments. "What got you here won't get you there" isn't just a call to acquire new skills but a profound invitation to reflect on our journey, understand our current location, and consciously adapt to elevate toward even more significant accomplishments and deeper understanding.

Let this book serve not only as a reflection of your past achievements but as a beacon guiding you towards greater heights. Remember, the journey of self-improvement and personal growth never truly ends; each new chapter in your life will demand a different version of you. Are you ready to rise to the occasion? Let this be your fourth call to action: to embrace this ethos of perpetual learning and self-reflection. Consider where you stand today and where you wish to go. Identify what new skills, understandings, or changes in perspective will you need to adopt to continue ascending in life.

As you continue to reflect on this book and its characters, consider the Ajanis, Zuris, and Olas in your own life. Think about safaris you've been on in your life and the tour guides that led you along. Think about the villages you've been a part of and the elders who have guided you toward your purpose and fulfillment. Each person and each experience carry a piece of your journey and a lesson in your unfolding story.

My hope is that this book not only entertains but also enlightens, offering new perspectives on the everyday challenges and triumphs we face. May it inspire you to ask 'why' and to delve deeper into your understanding of yourself and the world around you. May it also inspire you to embrace the myriad of roles you play in the lives of others and in your personal and spiritual growth.

As we close this chapter together, remember that the journey is never truly over. Each ending is a new beginning as well as a chance to apply the wisdom we've gathered, to plant new seeds, and to watch those seeds grow into the next chapters of our lives, rich with potential and brimming with possibility. Asking "why" is not just about seeking answers, but about understanding our place in a larger narrative, one that we co-author with every decision and inquiry. It is in this continuous cycle of questioning and discovery that we find our true purpose and forge paths that lead to deeper fulfillment and understanding.

ABOUT THE AUTHOR

Victory Gurley Jr, a dedicated father, creative, and serial entrepreneur, has a life story that reads like an inspirational novel. He has continually pursued new horizons, evident from his time as a U.S. Navy veteran, to his various business ventures, to his dynamic career in real estate across the sunny vistas of Florida, where he now resides.

Vic's journey through academia saw him making the bold decision to drop out of college not once, but twice as a testament to his belief in himself and pursuing practical experience over traditional pathways. This choice paved the way for a career filled with entrepreneurial ventures, leading him to be recognized as one of the Top 10 Under 40 in Tampa Bay in 2023.

As a community leader and serial entrepreneur, Vic has not only shaped his career but also molded the paths of others. He mentors both youth and adults, guiding aspiring entrepreneurs through the nuances of elevating their businesses and navigating their personal journeys towards success. His lifestyle brand, REAL—standing for Rich Even After Losses—encapsulates his philosophy of enduring and growing, regardless of life's challenges.

His commitment to community and innovation has also earned him the prestigious 2024 Presidential Lifetime Achievement Award. Vic's impact and story have been featured in prominent publications including Tampa Magazine, Orlando Voyager Magazine, and CanvasRebel Magazine, highlighting his influence in business and community leadership.

Visit www.RichEvenAfterLosses.com to learn more and to access the *Why Don't We Ask Why?* Workbook, to help you evaluate and learn to apply the wisdom and principles highlighted throughout this book.

ACKNOLEDGEMENTS

Throughout my life I have seen a lot, done a lot, and have enough experiences for multiple lifetimes. Through it all, there have been individuals, both well-intentioned and ill-intentioned, in every stage of my life that have contributed to the man I am today, both consciously and unconsciously.

Thank you to my son, Veremiah Gurley, for teaching me patience and showing me how to love unconditionally.

Thank you to my mother for always believing in me and being my biggest supporter.

Brothers: Victorious Gurley, Jaden Gurley, Brandon Gurley, Chris Bruce, Quest, Mike Mike Johnson, Steven "Dougie" Jones, Spencer Elosiebo, Shawn Smith, Brian Keese, Terrence "The King of Security" Carter, Chris Lee.

Women of my life: Grandmama Rita, Grandmama Roni, Auntie Angie, Dara Thammavong, Shariah Sanders, Tiffon Harris, MarChina Latrese, Toya Drew.

Men of my life: Granddaddy Michael, Uncle Tyrone, Clarence "Mr. Jack" Jackson, John "JFK" Kennedy (not the president lol), Sam McDuffie, Neil Lee,

Gone but not forgotten: Brandon Gurley, Luberta "Nana" Russell, Auntie Vivian "Boom Boom," Granddaddy JR, Grandma Cassandra, Grandpa Edward.

Thank you to all of my Instagram, Facebook, YouTube, and TikTok supporters who like and share my content and everyone that has ever purchased any of my products and/or services.

Thank you to my R.E.A.L family.

Thank you to Eric Thomas, Gary Vee, Myron Golden, Dick Gregory, Jordan Peterson, Bob Proctor, and Sadhguru for the motivation and words of wisdom.

I give honor to God for continuing to lead, guide, and protect me along this journey.

Thank you to Victory Gurley Sr. We have never really seen eye to eye, but I would be remiss if I did not recognize your contributions to the man I've become.

Lastly, I want to give a very special thanks to anyone who has ever doubted me, thrown dirt on my name, or prayed on my downfall. I am sending you all healing energy and may you all be blessed.

With Much Gratitude,

Vic
#StayREAL

Made in the USA
Columbia, SC
22 June 2024

f8c1b83a-5a10-4b36-a4bc-abb3ed90dc90R01